W9-DDZ-811

A teacher's guide to

CHARLES DARWIN

His life, journeys and discoveries

Caroline Overy

ENGLISH HERITAGE

CONTENTS

ABOUT THIS BOOK

English Heritage Photo Library

Watercolour of Down House and garden.

Wellcome Institute Library, London.

Charles Darwin

Societies have always been interested in the origin of the world and of the human race and many explain it as an act of providential design. Charles Darwin was not the first to challenge the Judaeo-Christian doctrine of the creation with the concept of evolution, but his was the first voice to convince. His experimentation, collection of vast quantities of data and proposal of the mechanism by which evolution occurs – natural selection – published in his major work, *On the Origin of Species,* gave evolutionary theory credibility and respectability.

The publication of *Origin* in 1859 led to much controversy and debate since the theory of evolution attacked the foundation of Christian belief, yet it also encapsulated the Victorian idea of progress. By the time of Darwin's death in 1882, most scientists had accepted the theory of evolution and he was hailed as a national hero and given a state burial in Westminster Abbey. Contemporary newspapers claimed that the country *'had lost a man whose name is a glory to his country'*, *'one who*

has brought such honour to the English name, and whose death is lamented throughout the civilised world', *'the greatest Englishman since Newton'.*

Today his theories are still controversial. Many scientists consider that his theory of evolution by natural selection provides the basis for understanding the development of life on earth, while others think that it is misguided and should be modified or abandoned. More has been written about this man than

any other scientist. A vast amount of archive material in the form of his letters, notebooks and journals survives in Cambridge University. His house in Downe, Kent, recently restored and refurbished, is open to the public.

This book aims to:

■ introduce teachers and pupils to Charles Darwin, his life and work at Down House, his voyage on the Beagle, and his evolutionary theory

■ set his ideas within the wider context of the nineteenth century

■ link the subject areas to the National Curriculum, particularly in history, science and English at various levels

■ provide ideas for activities for pupils.

The book is divided into three sections covering Darwin the man; the voyage of the Beagle; and evolutionary theory. Each section includes a variety of source material to illustrate the topic.

TIMELINES

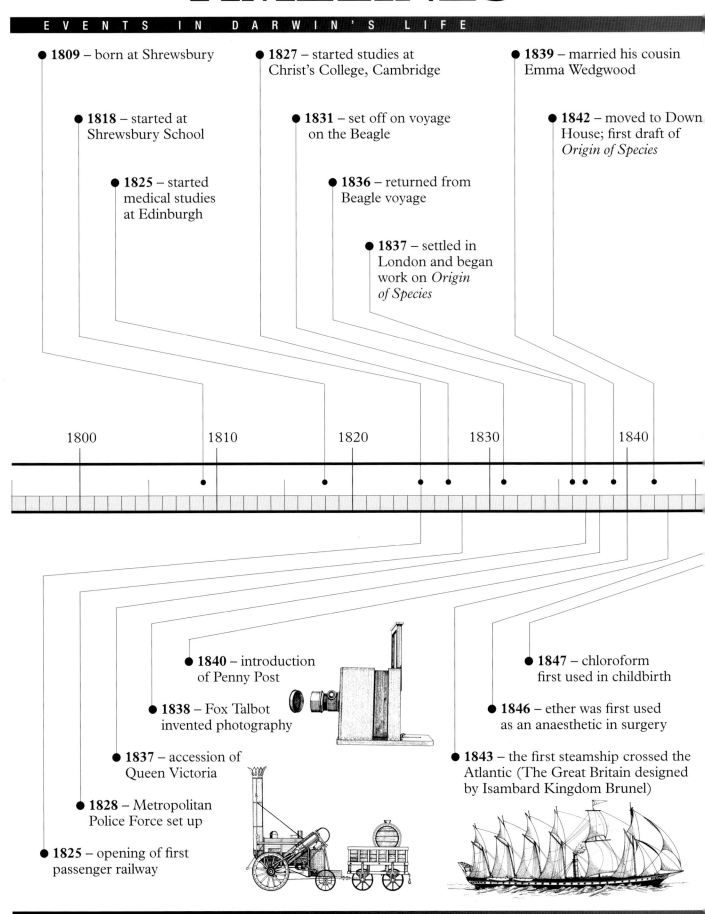

- **1809** – born at Shrewsbury

- **1818** – started at Shrewsbury School

- **1825** – started medical studies at Edinburgh

- **1827** – started studies at Christ's College, Cambridge

- **1831** – set off on voyage on the Beagle

- **1836** – returned from Beagle voyage

- **1837** – settled in London and began work on *Origin of Species*

- **1839** – married his cousin Emma Wedgwood

- **1842** – moved to Down House; first draft of *Origin of Species*

1800   1810   1820   1830   1840

- **1840** – introduction of Penny Post

- **1838** – Fox Talbot invented photography

- **1837** – accession of Queen Victoria

- **1828** – Metropolitan Police Force set up

- **1825** – opening of first passenger railway

- **1847** – chloroform first used in childbirth

- **1846** – ether was first used as an anaesthetic in surgery

- **1843** – the first steamship crossed the Atlantic (The Great Britain designed by Isambard Kingdom Brunel)

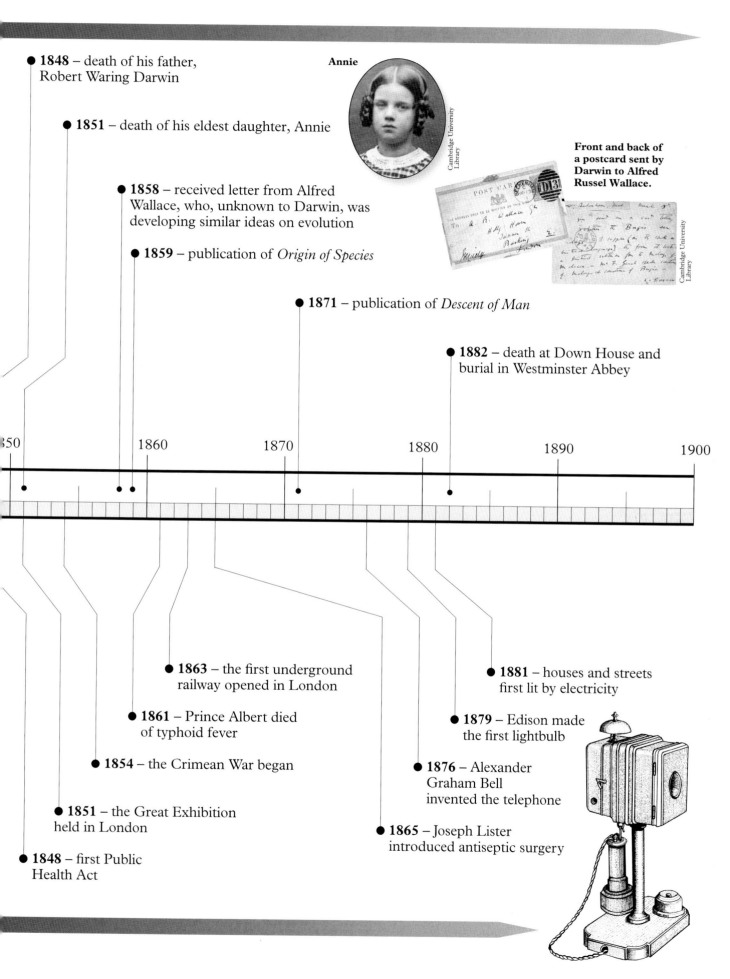

- **1848** – death of his father, Robert Waring Darwin

- **1851** – death of his eldest daughter, Annie

Annie

Cambridge University Library

Front and back of a postcard sent by Darwin to Alfred Russel Wallace.

Cambridge University Library

- **1858** – received letter from Alfred Wallace, who, unknown to Darwin, was developing similar ideas on evolution

- **1859** – publication of *Origin of Species*

- **1871** – publication of *Descent of Man*

- **1882** – death at Down House and burial in Westminster Abbey

350   1860   1870   1880   1890   1900

- **1863** – the first underground railway opened in London

- **1861** – Prince Albert died of typhoid fever

- **1854** – the Crimean War began

- **1851** – the Great Exhibition held in London

- **1848** – first Public Health Act

- **1881** – houses and streets first lit by electricity

- **1879** – Edison made the first lightbulb

- **1876** – Alexander Graham Bell invented the telephone

- **1865** – Joseph Lister introduced antiseptic surgery

CHARLES DARWIN'S EARLY LIFE

Charles Robert Darwin was born in Shrewsbury on 12th February 1809, the second son and fifth of six children of Robert Waring Darwin, a successful and wealthy physician in the town. Charles' mother, Susannah Wedgwood, died when he was only eight years old and he was raised by his older sisters, Marianne, Caroline and Susan.

his time reading, observing the natural world, and building up large collections of, amongst other things, beetles, bird eggs, shells, minerals and fossils. By the age of 15, he was old enough to follow pursuits such as hunting and shooting, on which he spent much time. After seven years Robert Darwin decided that Shrewsbury school was not suitable for Charles

young Darwin was soon spending his time collecting, dissecting and observing marine creatures. He became acquainted with other men interested in natural science, notably the zoologist, Robert Grant (1793-1874). At that time Grant was regarded as one of the country's most promising young naturalists, and he inspired Darwin's interest in marine

Robert Waring Darwin, Charles' father.

Edinburgh University

SCHOOL DAYS (1818-1825)

Charles spent a short time at a local day school and then, in 1818, was sent as a boarder to nearby Shrewsbury School. Charles was bored with the most part of his school education which concentrated on the classics, with much rote learning and recitation. One subject, however, which did engage his interest was chemistry: *'The subject interested me greatly .... This was the best part of my education at school, for it showed me practically the meaning of experimental science'.*

The head-master of the school, Dr Butler, rebuked Charles for wasting his time over 'such useless subjects'. Charles spent much of

'you care for nothing but shooting, dogs, and rat-catching, and you will be a disgrace to yourself and all your family'. So, at the age of 16, Charles was sent to Edinburgh University to study medicine.

EDINBURGH (1825-1827)

Although Edinburgh was one of the most prestigious medical schools in the world, Darwin's formal medical studies were not a success. He found the lectures intolerably dull, was greatly distressed by some of the cases in the clinical wards and also found he was unable to watch gruesome surgical operations (see page 27).

At this time Edinburgh was also a centre of marine biology and the

invertebrates. Darwin read widely and regularly attended the meetings of the Plinian Society, an academic club at which students read and discussed papers on natural science. It was also while he was in Edinburgh that he met the black taxidermist John Edmonston, formerly a slave in South America, who taught him to skin and stuff birds and mammal specimens. This skill was to stand him in good stead for his later exploits.

In 1827 Robert Darwin, aware that his son was unlikely to have a successful medical career, again suggested a career-move, this time to the Church of England, where Charles could have a 'respectable' career as a clergyman. After some consideration Darwin agreed and, at the end of 1827, went to Christ's College, Cambridge.

CAMBRIDGE (1827–1831)

Darwin spent three years at Cambridge studying mathematics, classics and divinity. These were of marginal interest to him but, despite being poor at mathematics, his hard work in the other two subjects led to a respectable BA degree in 1831. Of his time at Cambridge Darwin wrote: *'During the three years which I spent at Cambridge my time was wasted, as far as academical studies were concerned, as completely as at Edinburgh and at school… from my*

Christ's College, Cambridge

passion for shooting and for hunting and when this failed, for riding across country I got into a sporting set including some dissipated low-minded young men. We used often to dine together in the evening… and we sometimes drank too much, with jolly singing and playing at cards after-wards. I know that I ought to feel ashamed of days and evenings thus spent, but as some of my friends were very pleasant and we were all in the highest spirits, I cannot help looking back to these times with much pleasure'.

Darwin's interest in natural history did not wane whilst at Cambridge; he avidly collected beetles, forming a beetle brigade with his friends, and he eagerly attended lectures and field excursions by the clergyman and

DARWIN & his HOBBY.

These sketches were drawn by an undergraduate who collected beetles with Darwin.

Go it Charlie !

botanist, Professor John Stevens Henslow. It was Henslow who encouraged Darwin's scientific education. During his last year at Cambridge Darwin was greatly influenced by two books, Alexander von Humboldt's *Personal Narrative* which described his voyages to South America and inspired Darwin to travel, and Sir John Herschel's *Preliminary discourse on the study of natural philosophy,* which stirred in him *'a burning zeal to add even the most humble contribution to the noble structure of Natural Science'.* It was at this time that Darwin's interests began to include geology. He became friendly with one of the country's leading geologists, Adam Sedgwick, who aroused Darwin's

interest in the formation of the earth. In a university vacation in 1831 he accompanied Sedgwick on an expedition to North Wales where he learnt to interpret the geological strata of a region. On returning home from this trip, Darwin found a letter from Henslow inviting him to accompany Captain Fitzroy on his voyage on the Beagle. Thus, in December 1831 Darwin set off on a trip which was to last five years and take him around the world (see page 28).

DARWIN'S MARRIAGE AND LIFE IN LONDON

In October 1836 Darwin returned to England. After spending a few months in Cambridge he realised that to make his name he would have to move to London: *'I grieve to find how many things make me see the necessity of living for some time in this dirty odious London'.* In March 1837 he moved to Great Marlborough Street, London where he lived for two years working on the journal of his Beagle researches, published in 1845, and his geological obser-vations, published in three volumes – *Coral Reefs* (1842), *Volcanic Islands* (1844) and *South America* (1846). Darwin was heavily

(continued on page 10)

EDUCATIONAL APPROACHES

Darwin's family tree

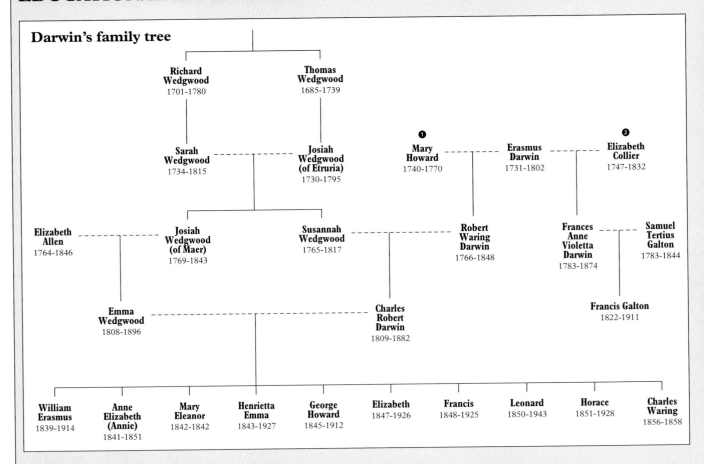

■ Using evidence

Ask pupils to choose an incident that affected their own lives, that they remember well and that made a great impression on them. Ask them to write three short accounts of the same event; one as they might write about it in a diary which they keep locked away; another as they might write about it in a letter to their parents, and a third as they might describe the event to an unknown audience – perhaps as an account for a newspaper.

Make sure the accounts are untitled, and ask pupils to swop with a partner to identify which account was written for which audience, giving reasons for their choices. This should lead to discussions about use of vocabulary, formal and informal sentence structure and detailed information as well as how much personal feeling and response is included in each piece.

Pupils could then discuss how we know about Darwin – autobiographical writing biographies, diaries, letters, and portraits. Ask them to think about the different levels of information we could gather from different sources. As an initial resource you could compile a dossier on Darwin by photocopying some of the longer quotations in this book, which give contemporary impressions both from Darwin's own words and from those who knew him well.

■ Life expectancy

Ask your pupils to study Darwin's family tree and to work out the size of his family, lifespan of individuals and average lifespan of his children. They could compare their findings with statistics from different levels of society in the mid-nineteenth century and with current statistics. The differences should lead to discussion about developments in medicine (see pages 20-24), public health and changes in society's expectations on family size and standards of living.

■ Family history

Your pupils could research and produce their own family trees, using the template opposite as a starting point. The personal family tree could provide the focus for an investigation into family history, perhaps even going back as far as the Victorian period. Pupils could make comparisons between their own family and Darwin's family. There is also scope for investigations in mathematics, in looking at the number of ancestors we have as we go further and further back into the past. Pupils will notice that each successive generation doubles the number of forebears, until a stage is reached where we each have more ancestors than the estimated population in the world. How could your pupils explain this?

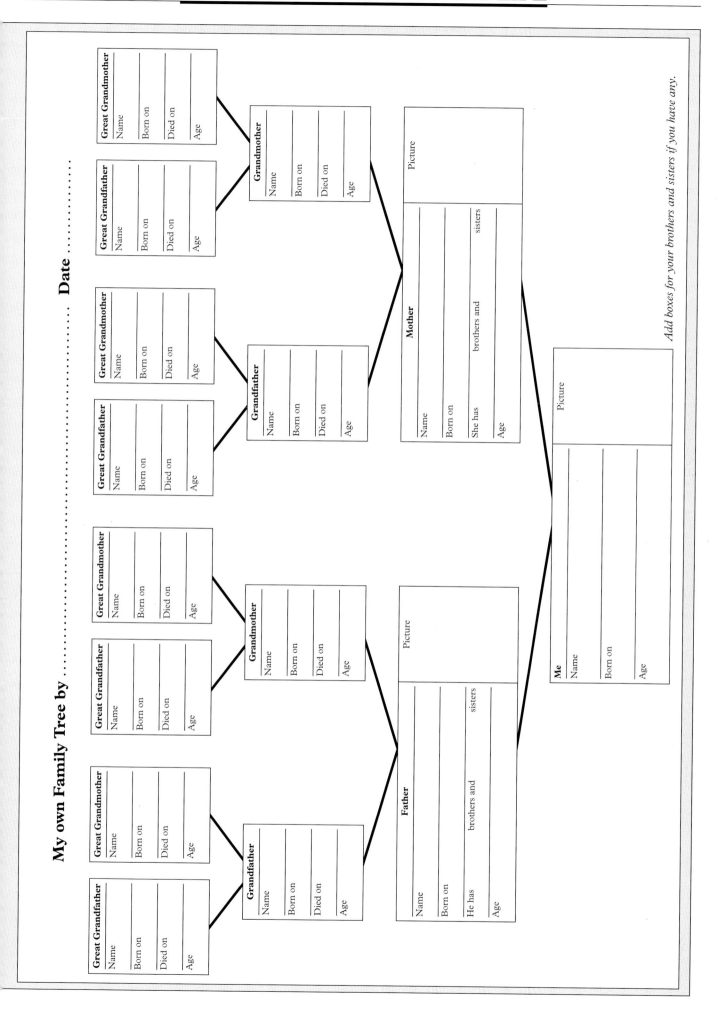

My own Family Tree by .... Date ....

Great Grandfather
Name
Born on
Died on
Age

Great Grandmother
Name
Born on
Died on
Age

Great Grandfather
Name
Born on
Died on
Age

Great Grandmother
Name
Born on
Died on
Age

Great Grandfather
Name
Born on
Died on
Age

Great Grandmother
Name
Born on
Died on
Age

Great Grandfather
Name
Born on
Died on
Age

Great Grandmother
Name
Born on
Died on
Age

Grandfather
Name
Born on
Died on
Age

Grandmother
Name
Born on
Died on
Age

Grandfather
Name
Born on
Died on
Age

Grandmother
Name
Born on
Died on
Age

Father
Picture
Name
Born on
He has   brothers and   sisters
Age

Mother
Picture
Name
Born on
She has   brothers and   sisters
Age

Me
Picture
Name
Born on
Age

Add boxes for your brothers and sisters if you have any.

9

involved in the Geological Society, the most active scientific society in the country, where he delivered various papers and became Secretary in 1838. He conversed with leading scientists of the day – the geologist Charles Lyell, the anatomist Richard Owen (who later became an opponent of Darwin's views), the biologist and traveller Joseph Hooker, Thomas Henry Huxley, Alexander von Humboldt, J F W Herschel and the mathematician, Charles Babbage. It was during this period of living in London that Darwin began to keep his notebooks on the transmutation of species which eventually led to the theory of natural selection, the outline of which had been comprehensively written by 1842.

It was not only science, however, that occupied his thoughts at this time; in 1838 Darwin was contemplating the prospect of marriage. Pencil notes assessing its pros and cons were scrawled on a piece of paper (see below).

Emma Wedgwood at the time of her marriage to Charles Darwin.

In November 1838, Darwin proposed marriage to his cousin Emma Wedgwood, daughter of Josiah Wedgwood II and Elizabeth Allen, to the delight of the two families. They were married on 29 January 1839, and moved to a house in North Gower Street. Within a year William Erasmus, the first of their ten children, was born. Emma was a deeply religious woman, who went to church regularly and brought their children up in the Christian faith. Darwin, although advised not to reveal his views on religion, was always open with his wife, and letters written during her married life show that it distressed her that her faith was not shared. Despite their conflicting beliefs they loved each other dearly; Darwin in his autobiography wrote *'She has been my greatest blessing, and I can declare that in*

Charles Darwin and his eldest son William, in 1842.

my whole life I have never heard her utter one word which I had rather have been unsaid… I marvel at my good fortune that she, so infinitely my superior in ever single moral quality, consented to be my wife'.

The Darwins lived in London for three years eight months, during which time Darwin claims to have done *'less scientific work … than during any other equal length of time in my life'*. The greater part of his work at this time was on his theory of the formation of barrier reefs and atolls. He also continued to supervise the publication of his *Zoology of the Voyage of the Beagle* (published between 1838 and 1843). During this period in London, Darwin experienced several periods of ill-health (see page 20). For his health to recover, he realised that he would have to leave the city and the pressures of work, for the solitude of the country. In 1842 the family moved from London to Down House, in the village of Downe, just outside Bromley, Kent.

CHARLES' PROS AND CONS IN HIS OWN WORDS

'This is the question

Marry

Children – (if it please God) – constant companion, (friend in old age) who will feel interested in one, object to be beloved and played with – better than a dog anyhow – Home, and someone to take care of house – Charms of music and female chit-chat. These things good for one's health. Forced to visit and receive relations but terrible loss of time.

My, God it is intolerable to think of spending one's whole life, like a neuter bee, working, working and nothing after all. – No, no won't do. – Imagine living all one's day solitarily in smoky dirty London House. – Only picture to yourself a nice soft wife on a sofa with good fire, and books and music perhaps – compare this vision with the dingy reality of Grt Marlboro' St. Marry – Marry – Marry. Q.E.D.

Not marry

No children, (no second life) no one to care for one in old age. – What is the use of working without sympathy from near and dear friends – who are near and dear friends to the old except relatives. Freedom to go where one liked – Choice of Society and little of it. Conversation of clever men at clubs. – Not forced to visit relatives, and to bend in every trifle – to have the expense and anxiety of children – perhaps quarrelling. Loss of time – cannot read in the evenings – fatness and idleness – anxiety and responsibility – less money for books etc – if many children forced to gain one's bread. – (But then it is very bad for one's health to work too much) Perhaps my wife won't like London; then the sentence is banishment and degradation with indolent idle fool'.

THE DARWINS AND THE WEDGWOODS

Darwin's grandfathers were both notable figures of the eighteenth century.

ERASMUS DARWIN (1731–1802)

Darwin's paternal grandfather was the doctor, scientist and poet, Erasmus Darwin. Erasmus studied medicine at the Universities of Cambridge and Edinburgh and, after unsuccessfully attempting to establish a practice in Nottingham, moved to Lichfield, that time a more famous town than

Erasmus Darwin

Birmingham. Here he built up a successful medical practice, becoming one of the most eminent provincial physicians of his day.

In 1766 Darwin co-founded the Lunar Society (see below), in the 1770s the Lichfield Botanic Society and, after moving to Derby in 1783, The Derby Philosophical Society, at which members discussed science and applied technology. Erasmus Darwin was also an inventor and designed amongst other things a 'lock for navigation' and a horizontal windmill, adopted by Josiah Wedgwood for grinding flints and colours. He published several works, some, such as *The Botanic Garden* (1789-91), written in verse.

This covered not only botany but also other branches of science such as geology, astronomy, chemistry and technology.

Although it was Charles Darwin who convinced the world of evolution, his grandfather had written on the subject in the previous century. In *The Temple of Nature,* first published after his death in 1803, Erasmus Darwin put forward his own ideas on evolution, including the view that existence was governed by nature rather than God. These ideas led to Erasmus being labelled an atheist.

JOSIAH WEDGWOOD (1730-1795)

Darwin's maternal Grandfather was the Staffordshire pottery designer and manufacturer, Josiah Wedgwood. Wedgwood converted what was until this time a semi-domestic process into a substantial industry. He used the raw materials and fuel resources of the Midlands, financed canal construction to aid transport and built his factory on a large scale. His designs catered for

Josiah Wedgwood

everybody. At one end of the market he established a reputation for high quality products which appealed to the rising European bourgeoisie, and continental factories suffered as a result

of his competition. At the other end of the market he produced ware for the growing mass market of industrialised Britain.

For his ornamental vases, Wedgwood built his 'Etruria' factory (so called after the imitation Etruscan style on some of his wares) at Burslem and in the early 1770s the production of his functional ware was transferred there. In 1782 Etruria was the first factory in England to install a steam-powered engine.

THE LUNAR SOCIETY

Erasmus Darwin was a co-founder, and Josiah Wedgwood a member, of the Lunar Society which flourished in Birmingham from 1766. This consisted of a group of fourteen Midlands scientists and industrialists who met monthly, at the time of the full moon (hence they were known as 'lunaticks), to discuss technology, science and invention. Along with Darwin and Wedgwood, the other members were Matthew Boulton, Thomas Day, Richard Lovell Edgeworth, Samuel Galton jun., Robert Augustus Johnson, James Keir, Joseph Priestley, William Small, Jonathan Stokes, James Watt, John Whitehurst and William Withering.

Although these men kept no formal records, their correspondence reveals much about their activities. They were responsible for mechanical inventions in the design of power machinery used in factories and mills, the design and construction of a wide range of instruments as well as aspects of agriculture, medicine, communication and education.

The Society's activities were determined by responses to industrialism and its associated problems; it encouraged social reform, promoted free thinking and free enterprise and condemned slavery.

DOWN HOUSE

DOWN HOUSE

In September 1842, Darwin and his family moved from the disease and dirt of London to the Kent countryside, to Down House in the village of Downe (spelt Down until 1850) just outside Bromley. Here, Darwin lived for forty years carrying out his scientific experiments and writing.

LOCATION

Downe was not the Darwins' first choice of location. They had searched in Surrey but finally decided on Down House, the main attractions being its price and its quietness yet its proximity to London. Darwin was able to escape the social duties of city life but still remain in contact with the intellectual life there.

The village of Downe was cut off from the Weald to the south by a line of chalk hills (the North Downs) and a hill to the north formed a barrier against London. When Darwin moved there the village comprised about forty houses, a fourteenth-century church, an infant school, a grocer's shop, a butcher, baker and post-office. Down House itself was half a kilometre from the village and was situated in seven hectares (eighteen acres) of grounds, comprising fields and gardens. On first seeing the house, Darwin wrote:

'On fine day scenery absolutely beautiful: from close to our house views very distant and rather beautiful, but being situated on rather high table-land, has somewhat of a desolate air…The charm of the place to me is that almost every field is intersected (as alas is ours) by one or more foot-paths. I never saw so many walks in any other county. The country is extraordinary [sic] rural and quiet with narrow lanes and high hedges and hardly any ruts. It is really surprising to think London is only 16 miles off.'

THE HOUSE

Parts of Down House date from around 1681 but the main block of the house itself was probably built in the eighteenth century. It underwent several alterations over the course of the next century before Darwin first saw the house in 1842. In a letter to his sister Catherine he wrote:

'House ugly, looks neither old nor new. – walls two feet [0.6m] thick – windows rather small – lower story [sic] rather low. – Capital study 18 x 18, [5.5m x 5.5m], Dining room 21 x 18, [6.5m x 5.5m] – Drawing room can easily be added to is 21 x 15, [6.5m. x 4.5m] Three stories [sic], plenty of bed-rooms. … House in good repair…, Mr Cresy a few years ago laid out for the owner £1500 and made new roof. Water pipes over house and two bathrooms [see below], pretty good offices and good stalls… with cottage… I believe the price is about £2200.'

The house originally comprised a kitchen, scullery and store in the oldest part, on the ground floor a drawing-room, a dining room and study, and bedrooms on the two floors above. Throughout his time at the house, Darwin carried out various alterations. Shortly after moving in, he built an extension of a large octagonal bay up the west side of the house and covered the house with stucco. In 1846 a service wing was added, of which he said:

'Our grandest scheme is the making our schoolroom and one (or as I think it will turn out) two small bedrooms… The servants complained to me what a nuisance it was to them to have the passage for everything only through the kitchen: again Parslow's pantry is too small to be tidy, and some small room is terribly wanted to put strangers into… and all these things will be effected by our

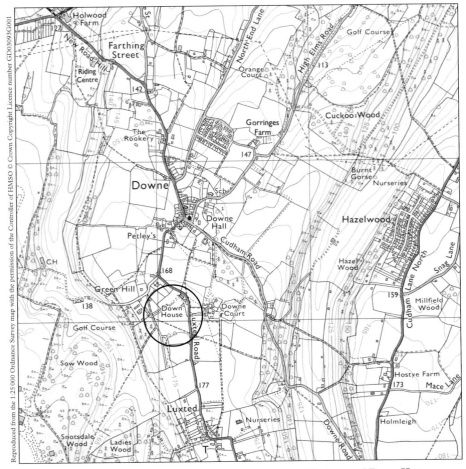

Detail from Ordnance Survey map showing the location of Downe and Down House.

plan… It seemed so selfish making the house so luxurious for ourselves and not comfortable for our servants, that I was determined if possible to effect their wishes.'

In 1858, a drawing room was built in the north-west corner of the house and a verandah was added in 1872. The verandah opened out from the drawing-room, had a glass roof and a row of lime trees to the west sheltered it from the afternoon sun. Following a stay, in 1858, in the health centre at Moor Park where Darwin had frequently played billiards, the game became an important part of his recreation. In 1859, shortly before the publication of *Origin*, he wrote to his cousin William Fox *'We have set up a billiard table, and I find it does me a deal of good and drives the horrid species out of my head'*. In 1876, a billiard room was added to the house.

For Darwin, the study was the focal point of the house into which he was able to retreat, away from the activity in the children's rooms

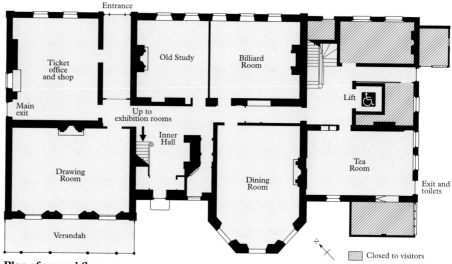

Plan of ground floor

Closed to visitors

Objects in Charles Darwin's study.

Above and below: The drawing room at the end of the nineteenth century and in 1930.

and the servants' quarters. It had two large shuttered windows which gave ample light for him to write, dissect and use the microscope, wooden shelves for books and files in an alcove by the fireplace and a lavatory enclosure in one corner. There was a circular table with a revolving top with drawers full of specimens and an iron-framed arm

The dining room towards the end of the nineteenth century.

house. There is a really fine beech in view in our hedge. The kitchen garden is a detestable strip and the soil looks wretched from the quantity of chalk flints, but I really believe it is productive. The hedges grow well all round our field & it is a noted piece of hay-land.'

On moving in, to increase the privacy, Darwin lowered the lane which overlooked the house by around half a metre. High flint walls were built, apple trees were planted and the removed earth was used to make banks and mounds around the garden. One mound was specially constructed in front of the door of the house to protect

chair. Darwin had even installed a mirror beside the window, angled so that he could see who was coming up the drive.

The study as visitors to the house see it today has changed very little from Darwin's time. Much of the original furniture remains, and the room is set out as it would have been when Darwin was working there. Other rooms on the ground floor which are open to visitors include the drawing room, the dining room, and the room where Darwin played billiards to relax. A small amount of original furniture remains, and this is displayed along with original artefacts associated with Darwin, his family and work. The rooms on the first floor contain exhibition material on Darwin's work and theories.

Water

There were no fixed baths at Down House; the bathrooms that Darwin refers to in the letter above were probably small rooms where a hip-bath could be placed without making a mess. The water would have been heated on the kitchen range and carried to the baths in cans. Darwin's grand-daughter, Gwen Raverat states in her book *Period Piece*, that in 1895 *'There was no bathroom at Down, nor any hot water, except in the kitchen, but there were plenty of housemaids to run about with big brown-painted bath-cans.'* There was a well and one hand pump for the house.

The grounds of Down House in the nineteenth century.

THE GARDENS

While living at Down, Darwin spent a great deal of time in the garden, experimenting and thinking. Over the course of forty years he made many changes and additions. Contemporary paintings, photographs and descriptions reveal what the garden was like. In 1842, shortly before purchasing the property he described the view from the drawing room:

'There are some old (very productive) cherry trees, walnut trees, yew, Spanish chestnut, pear, old larch, scotch fir & silver fir and old mulberry make rather a pretty group... There are quinces & medlars & plums with plenty of fruit & morello cherries, but few apples. The purple magnolia flowers against the

the house from the 'intolerable' north winds.

The ornamental aspect of the garden was for the most part typically Victorian with herbaceous borders, rose gardens and flower beds. There were six rectangular beds planted with, amongst other things, phloxes, lilies, larkspurs and verbenas. Darwin's daughter, Henrietta, recalls in front of the verandah the *'large flat lawn... slightly sloping upwards so that the flower beds made a brilliant effect from the window. The house became covered with creepers and shrubberies and orchards sheltered it from the south, where there was an open field'.* The gardens close to the house are still laid out in a way that Darwin and his family would recognise.

In his early days of residence,

English Heritage Photo Library

Jennie Fordham

The wormstone in the garden at Down House.

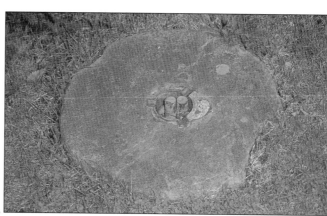

Jennie Fordham

Left: Darwin's 'thinking path' – the sandwalk at Down. Photograph taken by Leonard Darwin.
Below: Part of the Sandwalk today.

Jennie Fordham

Darwin created a new kitchen-garden on a strip of land taken from the Home Meadow, the old kitchen garden proving unsatisfactory, despite the optimism he displayed before buying the property (see above). Here he planted his experimental beds.

The Sandwalk, or 'thinking path', was created in 1846 on a strip of land in the south corner of home meadow. The land was planted with trees – hazel, alder, lime, hornbeam, birch, privet and dogwood. A line of hollies ran down the exposed side. Emma Darwin planted wild flowers within the woodland – bluebells, anemones, cowslips and primroses. This path is described by Gwen Raverat as she remembers it as a child at the end of the nineteenth century:

'a path running round a little wood which he [Darwin] had planted himself; and it always seemed to be a very long way from the house. You went right to the farthest end of the kitchen garden, and then through a wooden door in the high hedge, which quite cut you off from human society. Here a fenced path ran along between two great lonely meadows, till you came to the wood. The path ran straight down the outside of the wood – the light side – till it came to a summer-house at the far end; it was very lonely there… at the summer

house the path turned back and made a loop down the Dark Side, a mossy path, all among the trees'.
It was strolling round this path that Darwin did much of his thinking. Whenever he was at Down, he would walk a number of times, which varied depending on the weather and his mood, around the Sandwalk between midday and one o'clock.

The year before Darwin's death, a tennis court was built in a strip of land beyond the orchard.

The scientific garden
Between 1851 and 1853 a garden tank and shed were constructed; these were probably connected to experiments with a system to distribute liquid manure over the garden and field.

In March 1855, work started on his pigeon house in which he carried out his experiments on breeding pigeons to substantiate his theory of natural selection

(see pages 46-50). In a letter to his eldest son William in April of that year, he describes the structure: *'The Pigeon House is nearly complete & really does not look very ugly; it is a hexagon & the wire net part an oblong 16ft 9inches [5m approx] x 10 ft, [just over 3m], & 9 ft [2.7m] high'.*
No physical evidence of the structure remains.

As he became engrossed in the study of orchids and bees, Darwin built a small brick hot-house which was completed in early 1863. In a letter to Joseph Hooker he claimed that *'it will be a grand amusement for me to experiment with plants'.* This incorporated a brick platform at window sill level and was heated by two lengths of pipe. The hot-house was extended in 1868/9 and again in 1881. After Darwin had purchased the land immediately north of the kitchen garden, a brick laboratory was constructed on the north side of the garden wall, though it appears that Darwin could not have had much use of it before his death in 1882.

Visitors to Down House today are able to see much of Darwin's garden. The wormstone set into the ground to demonstrate and measure the effect of the action of worms on the earth is still there. There is still a greenhouse set against the north wall of the kitchen garden, and visitors may walk along the path of Darwin's sandwalk. The mulberry tree still grows and fruits close to the house.

DOWN HOUSE AFTER DARWIN
After the death of Emma Darwin in 1896, the property was let by the family to various people. In 1907 it

The opening of Down House as a museum, 1929.

Pupils of Downe House School.

became a girls' residential school, – Downe House School. In 1921 the school moved to Cold Ash, Berkshire, and Down House was again let, this time to a Mrs Ram, who also ran a school on the site.

In 1927, the house was up for sale, and the British Association for the Advancement of Science argued that it should be preserved as a memorial to Darwin and his work. The idea was taken up by Sir George Buckstone Browne, a London surgeon who provided the funds for the purchase and preservation of the house. He spent many years restoring the ground floor rooms of the house,

presenting them as they had been during Darwin's time as far as possible. The house was first opened to the public in 1929.

In 1952 the Royal College of Surgeons took over the responsibility for maintaining and running the house as a continuing memorial to the work of Charles Darwin. By the 1990s the house was in need of major conservation, and English Heritage, with the help of a substantial grant from the Wellcome Trust, has been carrying out this work since 1996. The house and grounds are now fully open to visitors as one of the sites managed by English Heritage.

EDUCATIONAL APPROACHES

Where to live?

How do people choose where to live? Give pupils a list of the reasons why Darwin chose the house at Downe, and then ask them to consider the location of their own homes, either from their own individual point of view or bearing in mind the needs of their whole family. They should make a list of the advantages and the disadvantages of the location of their homes.

If you are able to take your pupils to Down House they could make their own list of advantages and disadvantages of living there from their own point of view, and compare these views with Darwin's own. This activity could be developed by asking pupils to write, illustrate and design a leaflet advertising Down House for sale as a family home. The outlines of the outside of the house could be used as a basis for your pupils' own observational drawings.

Reasons why Darwin chose to live at Downe:

■ close to London. Charles was anxious to remain in touch with scientific ideas, and often invited colleagues to visit him

■ good transport links to London (see page 19)

■ rural setting

■ healthier environment than London

■ space to carry out experiments

■ space to bring up a large family

■ close to village facilities, including the church for Emma.

Houses and homes

Comparisons can be made between the size and scale of Down House and pupils' own homes; some may live in Victorian terraced houses. Ask pupils to list the rooms in their own houses, saying what each one is used for. Then ask them to list the rooms in Darwin's house, and possible activities that these rooms may have been used for. Rooms today are much more multi-purpose than those in a middle-class Victorian home would have been. Older pupils can be asked to measure rooms and to make their own scale plans of individual rooms, or their entire house or flat, depending on their age and ability. If they use the same scale as that used for the plan of Down House (see page 13) it will be easy to make comparisons by cutting out their own plans and laying one on top of the other.

Downe village – past and present

The village of Downe still retains its rural feel, despite its proximity to the heavily populated areas of Bromley and Orpington on the outskirts of Greater London. If you are visiting Down House with your pupils, take the opportunity to visit the village of Downe which is only a short walk away (care should be taken on the narrow roads). You could enlarge the extract from the Ordnance Survey (1:25 000) map on page 12 and ask your pupils to follow the route they are taking, noticing landmarks on the way.

In the village your pupils can visit Downe Church where Emma was a regular worshipper. Ask them to look for references to the Darwin family in the church and churchyard. Darwin's long-serving butler Parslow is buried in the churchyard.

Your pupils could also carry out a traffic survey or survey of facilities in the village.

Down House: south west elevation

Donald W Insall & Associates Limited

Down House: north east elevation

Donald W Insall & Associates Limited

COMMUNICATIONS

TRANSPORT

The nineteenth century saw great changes in the transport and communication system across the country. In the previous century, the industrial revolution had led to road and waterway improvements in the form of turnpike roads, canals and river navigation and the advent of steam power. These improvements were eclipsed, however, in the early part of the nineteenth century with the emergence of a new transport system, in the form of the railway. 1830 marked the beginning of the 'railway era'. By 1843 the total railway mileage

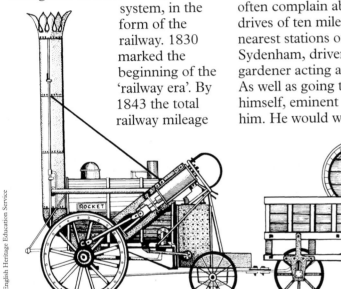

George Stephenson's Rocket.

was around two thousand miles; by 1849 it was around five thousand.

In 1842, when Darwin first arrived at Down House, the journeys to and from London would have been a coach drive of around 20 miles; in a letter to his sister, however, before buying the house, he noted the proximity of the station:
'Position about a quarter of a mile from a small village of Down in Kent sixteen miles from St. Paul's, eight and a half from a station with many trains; which station is only 10 [miles] from London. I calculate we were two hours' journey from London Bridge... a carrier goes weekly to London and calls anywhere for anything in London and takes anything anywhere.' The train

service from London was one means by which Darwin, in the seclusion of Down House, stayed in touch not only with family but also with the intellectual life of the city. In December of 1842, he wrote 'I hope by going up to town for a night every fortnight or three weeks, to keep up my communication with scientific men and my own zeal, and so not turn into a complete Kentish hog'. For the first years at Down, Darwin made such visits; his son Francis recalls that his father would often complain about the tiresome drives of ten miles or so to the nearest stations of Croydon or Sydenham, driven by an old gardener acting as a coachman. As well as going to London himself, eminent scientists visited him. He would write giving instructions on the best route. To Joseph Hooker he wrote in 1844:
'If you come by coach it is by the 'Down' Coach which starts at 3.15 from the Bolt-in-Tun, but I am sorry to say it is a very slow one, & you will not be at this house till past half past 6 o'clock. – I have unfortunately made an arrangement to use my phaeton [light carriage] on that day, but I have just written to try and alter it, & if I so succeed, I will... send the phaeton to station at Sydenham on the Croydon Railway: Trains leave at 1.20, 2.20, 3.20, both from London Bridge & from the Bricklayers arms [the terminus of the Croydon railway, which was opened in May 1844]; & if you start by the 2.20, you would arrive here at 4.30... it is a pretty drive to here from Sydenham'

The railways from London were gradually extended nearer to Downe village; in 1857 the South Eastern Railway was extended from Lewisham to Beckenham; in 1858, Darwin wrote to William Fox 'We shall be most heartily rejoiced to see you here at any time; we have now Ry to Beckenham which cuts of [sic] 2 miles & gladly we will send you both ways at any time'. By the second half of the 1860s the line had reached Orpington. To Professor John Tyndall in 1868 he wrote:
'your best route will be by S.E. Railway from Charing Cross to Orpington Station, which is four miles from the house... you will find 4.18 or 5.18 from Charing Cross convenient trains and if you let me know which I shall send a fly [one-horse carriage for hire] from here. If you come to Bromley (6 miles off) flys are plentiful.'

Charles Darwin was a share holder in the South Eastern Railway, as he was in many railways in Britain and the United States. His investments brought him a sizeable annual income.

The route from Downe to the stations would have been by a horse drawn carriage, either privately owned or using the omnibus service. The Downe Gazette published in 1951 at the time of the Festival of Britain records some of the memories of the older inhabitants of the village who could remember back to the late nineteenth century. A Mrs Gibbs described the horse-drawn bus service to Orpington and Bromley:
'[The Orpington] bus used to leave Downe at 8 o'clock in the morning, and took many of the business men to Orpington station, returning there in the evening to meet trains coming in about 6 o'clock. The Bromley bus went three times a day. These buses were of the closed type in winter, but in the summer were open brakes with canopy tops. The bus would hold about twelve people.'

POSTAL SERVICE

The other means of communication by which Darwin kept in contact with his family and scientists was by letter. The postal service was reformed in the late 1830s by the English administrator, Rowland Hill (1795-1879) who introduced the penny post. Although Hill was neither a postal official nor possessed experience of the postal system, he laboriously collected statistics to demonstrate that the main expense of the system was in the receiving and distributing, the cost of conveyance differing little with distance. He thus concluded that a uniform postal rate would be the fairest and in 1837 recommended that within the United Kingdom the rate for letters weighing under half an ounce (fourteen grams) should be only one penny. Any deficiency in the rate would be made up by the vast increase in correspondence, pre-payment, improved account keeping and a reduction in the expense of distribution. Regarding stamps he said *'perhaps the difficulties might be obviated by using a little bit of paper just large enough to bear the stamp, and covered at the back with a glutinous wash which by applying a little moisture might be attached to the back of a letter.'*

On January 10th 1840 the penny postal rate was introduced.

The correspondence between Darwin, his family, friends and other scientists are one of the main sources of information about Darwin's life and work. The nature of his work and ill-health rendered him particularly dependent on this form of communication. A calendar of the correspondence of Charles Darwin published in 1985 details some 13,925 letters written and received by Darwin,

Front and back of a postcard sent by Darwin to Alfred Russel Wallace.

and a team of editors are now publishing the letters. To date, ten volumes have been published covering the years 1821-62. The Darwin family rhyme was *'Write a letter, write a letter Good advice will make us better.'*

EDUCATIONAL APPROACHES

How to get there

Darwin was very helpful to his guests in giving them specific instructions on how to reach the village of Downe.

Start by asking your pupils to describe how to get to their school from various places in the area, as if they were giving directions to a stranger who did not have a car. Then ask your pupils to write a letter to a friend, preferably one who lives not too far away, explaining how to get to their own house, and how long their guest should allow for the journey.

You will need to have some reference material – local maps, rail timetables, details of bus routes etc for this to be an effective exercise. If you are visiting Down House with your class you could ask them to plan and cost the journey by public transport – are there any parts of the journey which cannot now be undertaken by public transport? How would your class recommend they reach Down House for their visit, bearing in mind the time taken, convenience and cost?

THE BROMLEY RECORD AND MONTHLY ADVERTISER.

[Registered for Transmission Abroad.]

No. 43. | DECEMBER, 1861. | Price One Penny.

Time Table—MID KENT.—DECEMBER.

WEEK DAYS—UP.

LEAVING												
Bickley	7.50	8.35	9.15	10. 0	11.25	1.30	3.30	4.30	5.30	6.30	7.30	8.25	10.35
BROMLEY	7.54	8.39	9.19	10. 4	11.29	1.34	3.34	4.34	5.34	6.34	7.34	8.29	10.29
Shortlands	7.57	8.42	9.21	10. 7	11.32	1.37	3.37	4.37	5.37	6.37	...	8.32	10.42
Beckenham	8. 2	8.47	9.26	10.12	11.37	1.42	3.42	4.42	5.42	6.41	7.39	8.37	10.47
London Br. arr.	8.35	9.20	9.50	10.45	12.10	2.10	4.10	5.10	6.10	7. 5	8. 5	9.10	11.20

WEEK DAYS—DOWN.

LEAVING												
London Bridge	6.55	7.40	8. 0	9.10	10.30	12.30	2.30	3.30	4.40	5.40	6.30	7.30	9.30
Beckenham	7.15	8. 2	8.32	9.32	10.56	12.56	2.56	3 56	5. 3	6. 3	6.56	7.56	9 56
Shortlands	...	8. 8	8.38	9.38	11. 1	1. 1	3. 1	4. 1	5. 8	6. 8	7. 1	8. 1	10. 1
BROMLEY	7.24	8.11	8.41	9.41	11. 5	1. 5	3. 5	4. 5	5.12	6.12	7. 5	8. 5	10. 5
Bickley arr.	7.30	8.18	8.50	9.46	11.13	1.13	3.13	4.13	5.20	6.20	7.13	8.13	10.13

The timetable for the London to Bromley line in 1861.

Pupils could

■ look at a copy of a local railway timetable and work out how long particular journeys take

■ use a map to work out the distances covered between stations.

It may be possible from a local library to get a copy of an old timetable for your own area – the journey times, frequency of service and even costs could be compared with today.

Design a stamp

Postage stamps are now such an accepted part of daily life it is difficult to imagine sending a letter without the pre-paid system. Many stamps are now produced to commemorate particular occasions. Pupils could be asked to design their own postage stamps to commemorate particular events in the history of their own school.

CHARLES DARWIN AND MEDICINE

In his letters and journals, Darwin wrote a good deal about his ill health and there has been a lot of subsequent debate as to the nature and cause of it. Returning from his Beagle voyage, during which he succumbed to various illnesses and ailments he spent the rest of his life suffering intermittently, with a multitude of symptoms ranging from headaches, trembling and joint pain to nausea, appetite loss, weight loss and ringing in the ears. Many of these seem to have been brought on by emotional stress at notable points in his life – on his move to London and overwork (1837), the birth of his first son and the responsibilities of marriage and fatherhood (1839), moving to Down (1842), the death of his father (1848) and the publication of *Origin of Species* (1859).

THE WATER CURE

Darwin was examined by a number of notable physicians of the day but none found any physical explanation for these symptoms. Since orthodox medicine did not help, it was suggested that he might benefit from Dr Gully's fashionable hydropathy treatment, or water cure, at Malvern. In March 1849 the Darwin family rented a house in Malvern whilst Darwin underwent the treatment. The treatment included cold showers and baths, wrapping in a wet sheet, steam baths and massage. In one letter he wrote: *'At present I am heated by a spirit lamp till I stream with perspiration, & am then suddenly rubbed violently with towels dripping with cold water: have two cold feet-baths, & wear a wet compress all day on my stomach.'* Nearly four months later he wrote: *'I consider the sickness as absolutely cured. And about 3 weeks since I had 12 hours without any flatulence,*

Malvern

Dr Gully

which showed me that it was possible that even that can be cured, as Dr. G. always said he could. The Water Cure is a grand discovery & how sorry I am that I did not hear of it, or rather that I was not somehow compelled to try it some five or six years ago.'

Back at Down at the end of June, in order to follow Dr Gully's instructions, Darwin built what he called the 'douche', a small house close to the main house which contained a bath-tub. With water drawn from the nearby well, he took daily water treatments. Darwin visited Malvern four more times, the worst time in 1851 with his seriously ill, ten-year old daughter Annie. Annie died while at Malvern, and after this Darwin could not bring himself to visit the place for another twelve years. He did however take hydropathic treatment again, this time at Moor Park in Surrey and Ilkley in Yorkshire.

DIARY OF HEALTH

Shortly after returning from his first visit to Malvern, Darwin started his diary of health in which, for the next five and a half years, he made daily entries about his health. Each day he summarised his illnesses for that day and the night. His most common symptoms were flatulence of varying intensity (noted on most days), boils, headaches, cold and skin conditions. The diary indicates that almost any event which changed his daily routine caused some illness.

Many theories have been put forward to explain Darwin's illness. Doctors at the time varyingly described it as a form of dyspepsia, a form of gout or a result of his sea-sickness on the Beagle. Since then theories have included his relationship with his overbearing father, neurasthenia, eyestrain, mental overwork, and depression. It has been suggested that he may have been suffering from arsenic poisoning taken in the form of Fowler's solution, which was freely prescribed by Victorian physicians for various complaints; Darwin certainly asked his father for a dose when he developed a skin complaint on his hands before setting out on the Beagle. It is

Five surgeons participating in the amputation of a man's leg while another oversees them, 1793.

Darwin's pill boxes

possible that he took this solution for much of his life. His illness has also been attributed to Chagas' disease. He had been bitten by a bug when in Argentina, and perhaps was infected by the parasite which attacks the heart. Possibly this led to his palpitations and 'tingling about the heart'.

MEDICINE IN THE NINETEENTH CENTURY

During Darwin's lifetime there were many important advances in medicine and surgery. With the introduction of anaesthetics, antiseptic surgery and public health programmes, the mortality

rate had fallen from 22.4 per thousand in 1838 to 19.6 per thousand at the time of his death in 1882; the average life expectancy at birth in England and Wales had risen from around 40 to 44 years for men and from around 42 to 48 years for women.

SURGERY
Anaesthetics

Prior to the 1840s there was no form of general anaesthetic other than opium, henbane or alcohol which, in order to be effective, were frequently given in lethal doses. Many patients died from medical shock during or after operations. In the 1840s, the

American dentist Horace Wells experimented with nitrous oxide and William Thomas Morton, a former partner of Wells, experimented with ether. In October 1846 Morton performed the first operation using ether as an anaesthetic. News of this reached Britain in the same year and the eminent surgeon Robert Liston succeeded in amputating a leg of an anaesthetised patient in 26 seconds.

Antiseptic surgery

Despite the introduction of anaesthetics in the 1840s the risk in surgery was extremely high. Sir James Simpson stated that a patient undergoing surgery was *'exposed to more chances of death than was the English soldier on the field of Waterloo'*. Wounds would frequently become infected leading to amputation or death – the mortality rate from amputations could be as high as 50%. This was the case until the surgeon Joseph Lister (1827-1912), a supporter of Pasteur's germ theory, introduced the concept of antiseptic surgery in 1865. Using a solution of carbolic acid and linseed oil, he washed a wound and dressed it with a sheet of tin foil to prevent evaporation. In 1870 he introduced his carbolic spray to *'destroy microbes in the air'*.

A sickly female, dying probably from tuberculosis, with the image of death standing next to her.

His techniques, however, were not readily accepted though his carbolic spray was eventually used by Queen Victoria and became fashionable. As his ideas later generally became accepted, the mortality rate following surgery fell to about 5%.

Darwin and surgery

When Darwin was studying medicine in Edinburgh in the 1820s he witnessed two operations performed without anaesthetic:
'I attended on two occasions the operating theatre in the hospital at Edinburgh, and saw two very bad operations, one on a child, but I rushed away before they were completed. Nor did I ever attend again, for hardly any inducement would have been strong enough to do so; this being long before the blessed days of chloroform. The two cases fairly haunted me for many a long year'.

CHILDBIRTH

In the mid-nineteenth century childbirth was made less painful with the introduction of chloroform. It was first discovered in 1832 but not used in childbirth until James Young Simpson, Professor of Midwifery at Edinburgh, gave it to his patients in 1847. It caused outcry with many physicians and churchmen insisting that the use of chloroform in childbirth was against the laws of God, quoting Genesis 3:16 *'In sorrow thou shalt bring forth children'.* This attitude lasted until 1853 when Queen Victoria asked to be given it on the birth of Prince Leopold. With the royal seal of approval, choloroform's use in childbirth became more common.

The other great advance in childbirth during the nineteenth century was the reduction in puerperal or 'childbed fever', which was a major cause of death for women at this time. Doctors believed that it was caused by a miasma or infectious vapour until in the 1840s Oliver Wendell Holmes, a gynaecologist and obstetrician in the United States and a Hungarian doctor Ignaz Semmelweis independently arrived at the conclusion that this fever was an infectious disease. What Semmelweis termed putrid particles were being transmitted from corpses by doctors going between the autopsy rooms and the maternity wards without washing their hands. With this realisation, he insisted that all students wash their hands before entering the ward. Within a year the death rate had fallen from over 29% to just over 3% and the following year to 1.27%.

Darwin and childbirth

In January 1850, while Emma Darwin was giving birth to her eighth child, Leonard, Darwin gave her chloroform. In a letter after the birth he wrote:
'The day before yesterday Emma was confined of a little Boy. Her pains came on so rapidly & severe that I cd not withstand her entreaties for chloroform & administered it myself which was nervous work not knowing anything about it or midwifery… It seems, she remembers nothing from the first pain till she heard that the child was born. – Is this not grand?'
From this time on Darwin regarded chloroform as the *'greatest and most blessed of discoveries'.*

INFECTIOUS DISEASES

Infectious diseases accounted for a vast proportion of deaths in the nineteenth century; childhood diseases such as diphtheria, measles, and scarlet fever which today are vaccinated against or if they occur can be treated, were then killers. Other diseases which were prevalent at the time are today very rare in the western world.

An 1828 caricature showing an elderly woman dropping her tea-cup in horror upon discovering the contents of a magnified drop of Thames water – a comment upon the purity of London's drinking water.

Tuberculosis

At its peak, tuberculosis killed more people, especially young adults, than any other disease, and was responsible for one in five deaths in the industrialised world. The disease was of an infectious nature and characterised by fever, a pale complexion, coughing up blood and wasting. Tuberculosis was also known as consumption. Although it attacked all classes of society it was particularly rife among the poor, with over-crowding in homes and places of work. It was thought that it was caused by stress and emotional factors. It was Robert Koch's discovery of the tubercle bacillus in 1882 and thus its infectious nature that marked a decline in the disease. By 1900 the number of deaths had halved.

DISEASE	1848-72	1901-10	1981-5
All causes	1000	1000	1000
Infectious diseases of which:	321	200	3
tuberculosis	146	84	1
typhoid & typhus	38	7	–
smallpox	13	1	–
measles	19	20	–
scarlet fever	57	7	–
diphtheria	na	11	–
whooping cough	20	16	–
influenza	3	13	–
cholera	10	–	–
Cancer	9	47	199
Diseases of the nervous system	129	117	12
Heart diseases	37	86	390
Bronchitis	66	72	28
Pneumonia	57	90	49

Proportional rates for selected diseases per 1000 deaths from all causes – males, England and Wales (taken from M. Nissel, People Count London: HMSO, 1987).

Annie, Charles' daughter.

Cholera

Cholera originated in India, spread through Europe and had arrived in London by 1832 where it caused the death of over seven thousand people. The disease then disappeared, returning in 1848 – a second epidemic which killed seven thousand in London in one month alone, and by 1849 had killed seventy-two thousand. In 1854, a London physician, John Snow, believing that cholera infected the body via the mouth rather than by inhalation, linked an outbreak in Soho to a nearby water pump. The Board of Guardians of the Parish agreed to remove the pump and the epidemic ended three days later. Despite Snow's results, his theories were largely ignored until Pasteur's work on germs and Koch's identification of the cholera bacillus in 1883/4.

Typhus and typhoid

Both typhus and typhoid flour-ished during the first half of the nineteenth century. The former which concentrated in areas of poverty and overcrowding was transmitted by the body louse, the latter was spread by infected water, milk and food, and affected both rich and poor alike – indeed, Prince Albert, husband of Queen Victoria died of typhoid in 1861. It was especially prevalent in areas not subject to rigorous public health regulations. Both diseases declined in the second half of the nineteenth century with rising standards of living and improve-ments in drainage, water supply

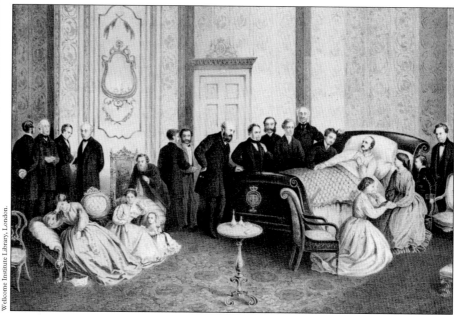

The death of Prince Albert at Windsor Castle, with the Royal family and household in attendance.

and housing. Deaths from typhus in London, for example had been reduced from seven hundred and sixteen in 1869 to twenty-five in 1885.

Public health

The leading figure in the public health movement of the 19th century was Edwin Chadwick (1800-1890). As a result of his involvement with the *Factory Act* of 1833 and the *Poor Law Amendment Act* of 1834, he concluded that ill health was the result of poverty. In 1842 he published his *Survey into the Sanitary Condition of the Labouring Classes in Great Britain*. Although not confined to the poor, infectious diseases ran rife in the over-crowded rapidly growing urban areas of Britain where only 12% had pure water supplies.

Chadwick's reforms which were pushed through parliament in 1848 included *'removing refuse from habitations, streets and roads and the improvement of water supplies'*. With increased sanitation in the 1860s and 1870s, slum clearance and rehousing coupled with advances in agriculture and food distribution, standards of health had improved dramatically by the end of the century.

DARWIN AND DISEASES

Darwin's children had many of the infectious childhood diseases. In 1858, his youngest child, Charles, died from scarlet fever at the age of eighteen months. After his death one of his nurses also contracted the disease and fearing there might be an outbreak, the Darwins moved away from Downe for much of the summer. In a letter to his cousin William Fox, Darwin wrote *'There has been another child die in the village of Down, which makes the fifth; so we rejoice we acted on your advice and left home'*.

Cholera also affected the Darwin family with the death of Fanny Wedgwood, Charles' cousin and Emma's sister. She died in the 1832 epidemic, while Charles was on the Beagle. It is possible that their daughter Annie Darwin died

from typhoid-fever at Malvern. Dr Gully states on her death certificate that the cause was *'bilious fever with typhoid character'.*

A doctor of a water cure establishment is unlikely to jeopardise his standing by giving typhoid as the cause of death. It is also possible that the Darwin family were concerned about the pollution of their own drinking water in the late 1860s, as there was a copy of a letter to *The Times* pasted into one of Darwin's medical notebooks reporting a typhoid-fever epidemic in the village of Terling, some 30 miles from Downe:

'By the latest accounts the fever has struck down 180 persons out of 900, the fatal cases being 16. These figures should awaken in the mind of every country householder an interest in the situation and condition of his wells… [wells] are still generally sunk where most liable to contamination, still often receive the contributions of sewers, &c., carelessly laid within a few feet or inches of the well wall'.

The water at Down House was all drawn from a well.

EDUCATIONAL APPROACHES

Looking at statistics

■ Use the mortality statistics in the table on page 23 to ask questions about changes in the prevalent types of disease and causes of death. What has caused the changes in the proportions of the various types of disease – advances in medicine, better sanitation and public health, the diagnosis of different diseases?

■ How useful is a table of mortality statistics as a resource for telling us about life in the nineteenth century? What do the figures not tell us? For example, pupils may notice that there seems to have been a great increase in the number of deaths from cancer; can they suggest any reasons to explain this apparent increase? How might they investigate this further? Today the incidence of tuberculosis is again increasing; can pupils offer any suggestions as to why this might be?

■ Pupils could present the information contained in the table of statistics in other, more visual, forms; for example graphs, pie charts and bar charts.

Common diseases

■ Ask pupils to make a survey of diseases experienced by the members of their class, including

common childhood infectious diseases, presenting the information in a variety of ways.

■ Then get them to carry out a similar survey on people from the previous generation – parents, friends of the family, teachers. If possible, extend this another generation back by surveying grandparents and their contemporaries. What similarities are there in the findings of the survey? Are there any differences? Have they, or their parents and grandparents been part of any preventative programme such as inoculation against certain diseases? Has this had any effect on the results of their surveys?

■ Entries in school logbooks often reflect the state of health of pupils in the school. References to major or minor epidemics will be noted, often with school closures. Smaller incidents may also be commented upon, such as pupils being sent home for being verminous or being without shoes. If your pupils have access to their own school log book they could investigate the number of times health matters are mentioned, make an analysis of the frequency with which certain diseases are recorded, and search for references to issues which relate to health, such as water supply, state of the building etc. Have these aspects of school life changed over a period of time?

EVERYDAY LIFE AT DOWN HOUSE

In some ways the Darwin household was typical of a wealthy Victorian family; in many respects however it was very different.

DARWIN'S ROUTINE

Like many Victorian families there was a set routine within the family; meal times rarely varied, and certain times of the day were set aside for different pursuits. For the forty years that Darwin was at Down House, with the exception of visits to London, holidays and visits to health spas, his daily routine seldom changed.

This routine continued as long as he remained moderately well, for week-days and weekends alike. Though, as Francis Darwin noted *'It was a sure sign that he was not well when he was idle at any other times than his resting hours.'*

DAILY LIFE

As in most wealthy Victorian families the Darwins spent much time in cultural pursuits, though with their liberal attitudes they were not restrained by convention in their views, or concerned that they were appearing ridiculous or unfashionable. Of a production of *Hamlet,* for example, Emma Darwin stated *'The acting was beautiful, but I should prefer anything to Shakespeare, I am ashamed to say!'* They read widely, both serious books, and novels which the family read aloud, the favourites being Jane Austen and Mrs Gaskell, whose works were read over and over again. Of novels, Charles remarked *'A novel according to my taste, does not come into the first-class unless it contains some person whom one can love, and if a pretty woman so much the better'* and *'novels, which are works of the imagination, though not of a very high order, have been for years a wonderful relief and pleasure to me, and I often bless all novelists.'* As well

Darwin's day

He would get up early and take a short walk around the garden, sometimes as far as the Sandwalk.

🕖	07.45	Breakfast alone
🕗	08.00-09.30	Work in his study
🕤	09.30-10.30	Reading letters or having family letter or a novel read to him
🕥	10.30-12.00	Work
🕛	12.00	Walk, whatever the weather, often accompanied by Polly, his white terrier. This usually began by visiting the greenhouse to look at the germinating seeds and experimental plants and was followed by circling the Sandwalk a number of times, keeping count of the times by means of a heap of flint stones, one of which he kicked away each time he passed. In the early days this used to be a fixed number of times but he later went round as many times as he felt strength for.
🕐	13.00	Lunch followed by reading the newspaper – probably the only non-scientific matter he read to himself. He had a considerable interest in politics. After this he would reply to his letters sitting by the fire in the large chair in his study, writing on a board resting on the arms. He kept all the letters he received and replied to them all, however troublesome they were.
🕒	15.00	A rest in his bedroom, lying on the sofa and smoking a cigarette, accompanied by Emma reading aloud a novel. He frequently fell asleep.
🕓	16.00-16.30	Another short walk
🕟	16.30-17.30	Work in the study
🕠	17.30-18.00	A short period of time in the drawing room
🕕	18.00-19.30	Another rest with novel reading and a cigarette
🕢	19.30	Dinner, after which he played two games of backgammon with Emma then read something scientific to himself for a while either in the drawing room or, if there was too much noise, in his study. He then followed this by listening to Emma play the piano and read aloud.
🕥	22.30	Retired to bed

The Darwin family at home in 1863.

Darwin records, Charles 'was not an indiscriminate child-lover'.

Compared with other Victorian families where children were to be 'seen and not heard' the children were allowed a great deal of freedom and were only constrained if they were in danger; punishment is rarely, if ever, recorded and corporal punishment, never. They were allowed to wander freely, they played noisy games and frequently disturbed Charles in his study, and there was generally a relaxed atmosphere about the house.

Francis Darwin relates the story of how Charles, finding Leo jumping about on the sofa, said: 'Oh Lenny, Lenny it is against all rules' to which Leo replied 'Then I think you'd better go out of the room.'.

When the children were young he would often

as novels, Charles also read *The Times* every day and subscribed to *The Gardener's Chronicle* and *The Athenaeum* and regularly read *Nature*. As a young man he would read poetry and Shakespeare, later, however, his interest in these pursuits waned. In his autobiography he stated that *'But now for many years I cannot endure to read a line of poetry: I have tried lately to read Shakespeare, and found it so intolerably dull that it nauseated me. I have also almost lost any taste for pictures or music'*.

Emma, as was common with many Victorian women, played the piano often to Charles, sometimes accompanying Francis on his bassoon. Within Downe village, the Darwins played an active role in village society. Emma's religion involved them in the local church; Charles helped organise a Friendly Club, was treasurer of the Coal and Clothing Club and, from 1857, served as a county magistrate.

AWAY FROM DOWN HOUSE

With the increase of efficient rail transport, people began to take annual holidays often in popular seaside resorts such as Brighton, Blackpool and Margate. For Darwin, however, his routine was essential to his well-being; anything beyond it caused pain and difficulty. The occasional day visits to London were arranged early in the day, the only time that Charles felt he was able to make the effort.

Pages from Horace Darwin's scrapbooks.

Short breaks of five or six days, often taken at the insistence of Emma when she realised that Charles was being overworked, were taken unwillingly. These periods were usually spent with relatives. There was the occasional longer holiday, for example spending six weeks on the Isle of Wight in the summer of 1868 and a month's visit to the Lake District which Charles and Emma took in 1879. As well as these breaks, Charles would also have periods away from Down at water-cure establishments at Malvern and Moor Park (see p. 20).

CHILDREN AND EDUCATION
Charles and his children

In common with many families of the period, Charles and Emma had a large family. Between 1839 and 1856 they had ten children, seven of whom survived to adulthood (see the family tree, page 8). They were devoted to the children who were a constant source of enjoyment although, as Francis

play with them, and as they grew up took an interest in all their pursuits. His extreme love can be seen in his reaction to the death of his ten-year old daughter Annie in 1851:

'We have lost the joy of our household, and the solace of our old age. Oh that she should now know how deeply, how tenderly we do still & shall ever love her dear joyous face'.

Despite the freedom the children were allowed and Charles' patience and tolerance, he never lost their respect. Francis, quoting his sister, stated:

'He cared for all our pursuits and interests, and lived our lives with us in a way that very few fathers do. But I am certain that none of us felt that intimacy interfered the least with our respect or obedience. Whatever he said was absolute truth and law to us.'

Education

As was usual for Victorian children, education of the boys was different from that of the girls. At around the age of seven Darwin's sons were sent to a private tutor and then on to a small prep school in Surrey before going to public school, although Darwin was not happy about removing the boys from family life. William was sent to Rugby, which Charles thought to be no worse than any other school. However he decided that too much time was spent on classics which had *'a constricting effect on William's mind and which checked anything in which reasoning and observation came into play. Mere memory seems to be worked. I shall certainly look out for some school with more diversified studies for my younger boys'*. They were sent to

Staff at Down House in the late 1870s.

Clapham Grammar School where the main subjects were mathematics and science rather than classics.

Both Charles and Emma were very relaxed over their daughters' education. Despite Erasmus Darwin (Charles' brother) and Fanny Wedgwood being highly involved in women's education and the foundation of Bedford Ladies' College, they themselves did not have their advanced views; Emma, years later, says in a letter to Henrietta in 1888 *'the fact is that I do not care for the Higher Education of women, though I know I ought to'*.

As in many Victorian families, when the children grew older a succession of governesses was employed at Down House, though none was very successful. Emma seemed to attract volatile and unstable women – one governess ended up in an asylum, one lasted only a couple of weeks, her

---

EDUCATIONAL APPROACHES

Daily routines

Darwin's set routine provides an interesting focus for investigation and comparison. Copy the timetable followed by Darwin and ask your pupils, in pairs, to analyse how much time he spent

■ working

■ relaxing with his family

■ taking exercise

■ at meals

■ sleeping.

Some discussion may be needed where there are activities which could fit into more than one category. Again, this information could be presented in diagrammatic form. Then ask each pair to estimate whether they spend more or less time than Darwin on each activity. Follow this up by getting them to calculate exactly the amount of time they spend, and compare this with Darwin. Are there any major activities that they follow that Darwin apparently did not?

The information extracted may be presented as a pie chart.

---

personality clashing with Darwin's, and the others, although very amiable and affectionate, seemed to lack teaching ability. The girls were mainly taught geography, music, singing and languages with no mathematics or science other than some basic botany. Henrietta wrote *'Our education, as far as book learning was concerned, was not of an advanced type; my mother apparently did not try and get the best possible teaching for us. But from our different governesses we learnt nothing that was not good and high-minded'*.

STAFF AT DOWN HOUSE

As in many Victorian households, there was a team of staff working at Down House. The Darwins were unusually courteous and thoughtful towards the welfare of their employees. The house was altered to suit their needs (see page 12) and as Francis Darwin recalled:

'As head of the household he [Charles] was much loved and respected, he always spoke to servants with politeness, using the expression would you be so good, in asking for anything. He was hardly ever angry with his servants; it shows how seldom this occurred, that when, as a small boy, I overheard a servant being scolded, and my father speaking angrily, it impressed me as an appalling circumstance, and I remember running upstairs out

of a general sense of awe'.

In return the staff were loyal and devotedly served the family. Of Darwin, Joseph Parslow, the butler, said:

'He was a very social, nice sort of gentleman, very joking and jolly indeed; a good husband and a good father and a most excellent master. Even his footmen used to stay with him as long as five years. They would rather stay with him than take a higher salary somewhere else. The cook came there while young and stayed till his death – nearly thirty years'.

Parslow himself served the family on a full-time basis for 36 years, from their marriage in 1839, onwards. Even after that he still carried out odd jobs for the family for many years. Joseph Hooker refers to him as *'an integral part of the family'* and Madame Sismondi, Emma's aunt, said that he was *'the most amiable, obliging, active, serviceable servant that ever breathed'*. The other staff included a cook, a gardener, a coachman, footmen, a housemaid, a nurse and as the children grew up, a governess. Frequently they would interchange jobs – *'in an emergency'*, Henrietta writes *'they would cheerfully work like horses; or any one would change their work; the cook would nurse an invalid, the butler would drive to the station, and anybody would go on an errand anywhere'*. Parslow is buried in the churchyard in Downe village.

INVITATION TO JOIN THE BEAGLE

THE BACKGROUND

The end of the Napoleonic Wars in 1815 brought a great expansion in world trade. The role of the Royal Navy was crucial both to offer protection to cargo-laden ships and to investigate and chart navigation. The Hydrographic Office of the navy had been engaged in survey work for many years but between 1808 and 1860 the work increased dramatically. As well as navigational information, vessels were expected to report on a wide variety of subjects – climate, topography, native flora and fauna, minerals, the inhabitants and their means of subsistence, pursuits, arts and language. The voyage of the Beagle, between 1831 and 1836, was one such expedition sent out to:

■ establish the exact longitude of Rio de Janeiro from which all other meridians and distances in South America could be measured

■ survey part of the coast of South America and Tierra del Fuego

■ report on the territory of the Falkland Islands which was the subject of a dispute between Britain and Argentina

■ continue round the world via the Galapagos Islands, Tahiti, Australia, The Cape of Good Hope, St Helena and the Ascension Islands concentrating on chronometric distances, (measurement of distance using astronomy and depending on the use of a very accurate time-measuring equipment – the chronometer).

The memorandum with the details of the voyage was sent to Captain Fitzroy by Francis Beaufort, the chief hydrographer, containing detailed instructions on meteorology and astronomy, a warning about the hostile nature of the natives of the Pacific islands and details of a classification to be used to indicate the state of the weather and wind force – the Beaufort Scale – which is still in use today.

DARWIN'S INVITATION

On his return from his geology trip to Wales with Adam Sedgwick, Darwin found the letter below from John Stevens Henslow.

John Henslow in 1849.

Wellcome Institute Library, London.

> *Cambridge*
> *21 August 1831*
>
> *My dear Darwin,*
> *…I hope to see you shortly fully expecting that you will eagerly catch at the offer which is likely to be made you of a trip to Terra del Fuego & home by the East Indies – I have been asked by Peacock… to recommend him a naturalist as companion to Captain Fitzroy employed by Government to survey the S. extremity of America – I have stated that I consider you to be the best qualified person I know of who is likely to undertake such a situation – I state this is not on the supposition of yr being a* <u>*finished*</u> *Naturalist, but as amply qualified for collecting, observing and noting anything worthy to be noted in Natural History… Capt. F. wants a man (I understand) more as a companion than a mere collector & would not take anyone however good a Naturalist who was not recommended to him likewise as* <u>*gentleman*</u>*… The voyage to last 2yrs & if you take plenty of books with you, any thing you please may be done – You will have ample opportunities at command – In short I suppose there never was a finer chance for a young man of zeal & spirit…*
>
> *J. S. Henslow*

Captain Robert Fitzroy was from an aristocratic background. He was twenty-six when he set out on the Beagle and was eager to have a well-bred gentleman as companion who could also act as

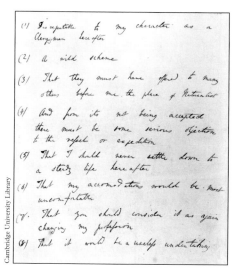

Charles' father's objections to the Beagle voyage.

the ship's naturalist. Henslow had suggested Darwin on account of his suitable social background and because, although not formally trained, he was a competent naturalist. Darwin was very keen to accept but first had to obtain permission from his father, who raised several objections. Charles noted these down:
'1) Disreputable to my character as a Clergyman hereafter
2) A wild scheme
3) That they must have offered to many others before me, the place of Naturalist
4) And from its not being accepted there must be some serious objection to the vessel or expedition
5) That I should never settle down to a steady life hereafter
6) That my accommodations would be most uncomfortable
7) That you should consider it as again changing my profession
8) That it would be a useless undertaking'
Charles showed these to his Uncle Josiah Wedgwood II (Uncle Jos), asking for his opinions. Josiah eventually managed to persuade Robert Darwin that natural history was a respectable pursuit for a clergyman to follow and the voyage might indeed open up an

alternative career path – that of a naturalist, ranking with other leading scientists.

Despite being political opposites, (Fitzroy was a Tory and Darwin a Whig,) and despite Darwin's nose apparently reflecting lack of firm character (Fitzroy believed in the science of physiognomy – that facial features reflect personality), Darwin was deemed a suitable companion and his position on board was confirmed.

DARWIN'S PREPARATIONS

Once the voyage was a certainty, Darwin started getting ready. In London he sought specialist advice. He met taxidermists who gave advice on preserving, stuffing and storing; he was shown how to seal jars using bladders, tin foil and varnish and how to pack skins; he was given pickling tips for marine creatures and advice on the best microscopes. In early September 1831 he wrote to his sister Susan: *Tell Nancy to make me 12 instead of 8 shirts: Tell Edward to send me up*

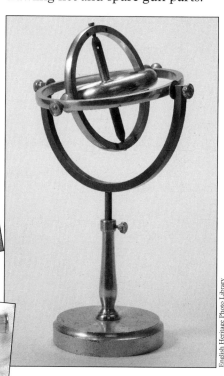

Darwin's compass

in my carpet bag… my slippers, a pair of lightish walking shoes. – My Spanish books: my new microscope, which must have cotton stuffed inside: my geological compass… a little book, if I have got it in bedroom, 'Taxidermy.' He bought himself a pair of pistols because Captain Fitzroy had recommended that he '*never went on shore anywhere without loaded ones*'. He went on board laden with specimen jars, chemicals, preservatives, dissecting tools and precision instruments including a clinometer, barometer, telescope and rain gauge, a trawling net and spare gun parts.

Some of the equipment Charles took on the Beagle voyage.

THE BEAGLE

The Beagle was initially a coastal carrier that had been converted in 1820 to a ten-gun brig – a class of small two-masted warships common in the first half of the nineteenth century. In 1825 the Beagle received her first commission orders to carry out a survey of the coastline of South America. Once back in England the ship was refitted once again for her second and most famous voyage.

The Beagle was stripped down to her timbers and rebuilt; there were many alterations including raising the upper decks which increased the headroom below decks to about six feet. The ship was given heavier rigging than before and the *'ropes, sails and spars were the best that could be procured…'* Seven guns were carried on the main deck (two more were added in Rio de Janeiro) which were of brass so as not to affect the ship's compass. She also carried small boats and a dinghy which were built for the purpose of the voyage. There were twenty-two chronometers – only

The Beagle

by having the exact time could longitude be established.

Instead of the common open-galley fireplace a stove with an oven attached was installed. This was safer and did not have to be put out in rough weather, which meant that hot food could be prepared when most needed. Lightning conductors were fixed on all the masts and as Darwin wrote *'no vessel has been fitted out so expensively and with so much care. Everything that can be is made out of mahogany.'*

Below decks there were two cabins, the captain's and the poop cabin which Darwin was to share with Stokes and a boy midshipman. The poop cabin measured three metres by almost three and a half metres, and was just under two metres high. It contained the ship's library, and a large table – the drafting table for the surveying officers, a chest of drawers, an instrument cabinet and a washstand. Two hammocks were slung above the large table. Despite referring to the cabin as a *'capital one'* – he describes his personal space as *'woefully small – with just enough room to turn round'*. The second lieutenant, who later became Admiral Sir Barthelomew Sulivan, described the cabin in a letter to Francis Darwin: *'The narrow space at the end of the chart-table was his only accommodation for working, dressing, and sleeping; the hammock being left hanging over his head by day, when the sea was at all rough, that he*

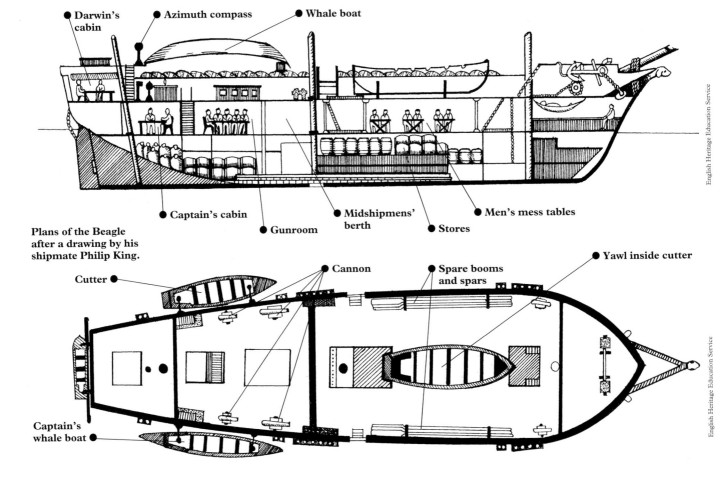

Plans of the Beagle after a drawing by his shipmate Philip King.

EDUCATIONAL APPROACHES

■ Ship design

Using the resource sheet on nineteenth-century ships, ask your pupils to compare the Beagle with other wind-powered ships which were being built at the time (see bibliography). Pupils could make simple balsa wood and fabric models of the different types of ship and rigging: one, two or three mast ships, square or triangular sails, fixed sails and those which turn into the wind, and could devise a simple test of efficiency for each design, using a low powered hair dryer to simulate windflow.

■ Organising a cabin

Using the measurements given for the dimensions of Darwin's cabin, and the description of the furniture it contained, ask your pupils to draw a scale plan or a 'net' of how they think the room might have been laid out, including any other items that they think Darwin might have had to store in his cabin. For instance, where would he have kept his scientific equipment? How would the room have been lit during the day and evening? This could be developed into the construction of a scale model of the cabin.

Your pupils might also find it interesting to plan and design their own cabin space for a long journey today, using the dimensions of Darwin's cabin as a starting point and assuming that they will be sharing the space with a friend. What personal belongings would they take with them if they were going on a journey for a year? How will cabin space be allocated? What leisure activities will need to be accommodated? How could clothes be stored? Encourage your pupils to use all the space available to them, and to devise innovative solutions to the problems of storage and privacy.

■ Food and drink

The planning and supply of provisions for Darwin's journey was carefully worked out to ensure that all on board had enough to eat and to remain healthy. Using the example of typical meals given below, ask your pupils to work out a sensible amount of rations to be provided for an adult male. If possible, bring a small supply of the kind of items taken on the journey, such as rice, dried peas, dried apples or pears, bread, pickled or preserved vegetables, and lemon juice and ask your pupils to weigh and itemise what they consider would be an adequate daily allowance. Pupils could then estimate the quantity of stores might have been required for one day for the whole ship's company, and from there how much would be needed for the length of the voyage.

instead of setting sail in October the Beagle finally left Plymouth on 27 December 1831. The crew of seventy-four included various specialists along with thirty-four seamen and six boys. Darwin was the naturalist. There was also a surgeon and his assistant, an artist, an instrument maker and a carpenter. There were also three passengers originally from Tierra del Fuego who had been brought back by Fitzroy on the previous voyage. They had been educated in England and were now being returned to their homes to spread Christianity and civilisation with the help of a missionary Richard Matthews.

For Darwin, the first few weeks at sea were miserable as he suffered terribly from sea-sickness. He wrote to his father:

'In the Bay of Biscay there was a long & continued swell & the misery I endured from sea-sickness is far beyond what I ever guessed at – I believe you are curious about it… Nobody who has only been to sea for 24 hours has a right to say that sea-sickness is even uncomfortable. – The real misery only begins when you are so exhausted – that a little exertion makes a feeling of faintness come on. – I found nothing but lying in my hammock did me any good. – I must especially except [sic] your receipt of raisins, which is the only food that the stomach will bear.'

Darwin was so sea-sick in the early weeks that Fitzroy doubted he would last the voyage.

Despite the cramped conditions Darwin wrote to his father *'I find a ship a very comfortable house with everything you want, and if it was not for the sea-sickness the whole world would be sailors.'*

might lie on it with a book in his hand when he could not any longer sit at the table. His only stowage for clothes being several small drawers in the corner, reaching from deck to deck; the top one being taken out when the hammock was hung up, without which there was not length for it… for specimens he had a very small cabin under the forecastle.'

As well as the two cabins there were small cubicles down either side of the lower deck, a gunroom, mess, galley, sick bay and the stores. The provisions which the Beagle carried included pickles, dried apples and lemon juice (to protect against scurvy), preserved meat, vegetables, rum and soap.

The date of departure was gradually put later and later, and

Daily routine on board the Beagle

8am	breakfast – Fitzroy and Darwin ate alone in the captain's cabin after which Fitzroy would make his rounds of the decks and Darwin, on a calm day would work on his marine animals – dissecting and classifying them, or if the weather was rough, he would lie down and read.
1pm	dinner – a vegetarian meal of rice, peas, bread and water.
5pm	supper – meat (fresh meat or fish when available), pickles, dried apples and lemon juice.

THE VOYAGE

The Beagle headed across the Atlantic to Brazil via Madeira (where they were unable to land due to unfavourable tides) and Tenerife (where they were forbidden from landing in case they were carrying cholera from the epidemic in England) and the Cap Verde Islands where Darwin made his first geological explorations. Crossing the equator, Darwin experienced the traditional ritual ceremony:

wandered for hours by himself marvelling at the *'elegance of the grasses, the novelty of the parasitical plants, the beauty of the flowers, the glossy green of the foliage…'*. It was here, however that Darwin first encountered slavery and he was appalled by it. In his journal he records several incidences of cruelty and it was on this subject that he and Fitzroy had their first argument, *'he defended and praised slavery which I abominated'*.

trap one day, preserve the next, and in the evenings would write back to England.

Sailing on to Montevideo the Beagle spent the next two years charting the area southwards. Whenever the ship was in port it was Darwin's usual practice to explore inland, making geological observations and collecting animal and plant specimens. He would usually travel on horseback accompanied by the gauchos, and either stay with local landowners or simply sleep under the stars. In various areas he found the fossil remains of extinct species, sloths, giants rodents and armadillos and noted the similarities to the continent's living species.

The traditional ceremony of crossing the equator, drawn by the Beagle's artist.

Wellcome Institute Library, London.

'Before coming up, the constable blindfolded me & thus led along, buckets of water were thundered all around; I was then placed on a plank, which could be easily tilted into a large bath of water. They then lathered my face & mouth with pitch and paint and scraped some off with a piece of roughened iron hoop; – a signal being given I was tilted head over heels into the water, where two men received me & ducked me …most of the others were treated much worse.'

THE EAST COAST OF SOUTH AMERICA

In February 1832 the Beagle sailed into Bahia (Salvador) in Brazil; the official survey began and Darwin's explorations began in earnest. He

On the final leg of the voyage from Rio de Janeiro back to England, Darwin wrote:

'I thank God that I shall never again visit a slave-country… I will not even allude to the many heart-sickening atrocities which I authentically heard of… It makes one's blood boil, yet heart tremble, to think that we Englishmen and our American descendants, with their boastful cry of liberty, have been and are so guilty.'

A few weeks later they moved on down to Rio de Janeiro; whilst the surveyors established the longitude of the city, Darwin spent two months observing the geology, marine life, vegetation, animals and insects – in one day he collected sixty-eight different species of beetle. He would collect, shoot or

TIERRA DEL FUEGO

The Beagle then went south to Tierra del Fuego where she left the three 'civilised' Fuegians who were travelling with them; they had learnt English, mixed in society and even been presented to King William IV. Armed with the rudiments of the Christian religion, supplies from the London Missionary Society and help from the missionary Richard Matthews, they were returned to their native land. Here, the inhabitants seemed to epitomise the nineteenth century view of the 'uncivilised savage'. On the Beagle's arrival, Darwin described the scene:

'It was without exception the most curious and interesting spectacle I ever beheld: I could not have believed how wide was the difference between savage and civilised man: it is greater than between a wild and domesticated animal, inasmuch as in man there is a greater power of improvement'.

Darwin, noting the difference between Jemmy Button, one of the three returning Fuegians, and the natives, found it hard to believe that *'he should have been of the same race, and doubtless partaken of the same character, with the miserable, degraded savages whom we first met here.'* After ten days charting and exploring, the crew of the Beagle

The three Fuegians who were resettled in an Anglican mission.

human nature and the 'savage' and 'civilised' races; his interest in the ability of humans to 'progress' from a state of 'savagery' to 'civilisation' was fundamental to his evolutionary theory and the notion of mankind being an integral part of the natural world.

THE FALKLAND ISLANDS

The Beagle then sailed on to the Falkland Islands which were the subject of a dispute between

Britain and Argentina. The Islands were of strategic importance for trade and were therefore to be surveyed accurately. Darwin passed the time collecting the alpine flora and fauna and studying the geology and fossil fauna of the area. He collected the tiny plant-like marine animals – zoophytes and coral polyps – which he dissected and thus came to realise that there was no sharp dividing line between the animal and plant kingdoms.

returned to find Matthews had had his goods pillaged and he rejoined the ship. Returning a year later they found that the three Fuegians had returned to their former way of life. This episode of the voyage prompted Darwin to think about

The cathedral at Concepción after the earthquake of 1835.

EDUCATIONAL APPROACHES
Into the unknown

The journey of the Beagle provides scope for geographical investigations into any of the areas which the ship visited, as well as material for studying physical processes such as subsidence, volcanic activity and earthquakes.

An interesting way to introduce your pupils to the scale and scope of the Beagle's voyage is to ask them to devise their own board game to represent the various stages and important events or discoveries on the journey. Older pupils might well be able to devise their own board game from scratch, using only a description of the journey (see Bibliography) and reference material about each place. However you may prefer to give your pupils a starting point or structure for their activity.

The layout and instructions on pages 36 and 37 are designed for you to photocopy for individuals or groups of pupils. You may like to copy onto brightly coloured paper, or to enlarge each page to A3 size. You will also need to copy the map on the inside back cover. If you decide to make this an activity for groups of four to six pupils, you could ask them to scale up their photocopy as a mathematical exercise, redrawing the grid onto large sheets of sugar paper. If you do this, make sure that the pupils scale up the picture squares using the same ratio they used for the board. Emphasise to your pupils that they must make sure that their game reflects the actual events of Darwin's voyage in the same order that they occurred.

The activity could end with the class playing the various games to judge, having decided on their own criteria, which best reflects the events of Darwin's journey.

Devising their game should encourage your pupils to:

■ put events in order, developing a sense of chronology

■ look at relative spacing of events over time, making sure that the whole journey fits onto the board

■ familiarise themselves with the position of the continents on a world map

■ use appropriate vocabulary to describe geographical or scientific processes and theories

■ research various aspects of Darwin's journey and work to find appropriate events to include in their game

■ understand the scale and scope of the Beagle's journey

■ use their imagination and design skills

■ develop decision-making and negotiation skills.

THE WEST COAST OF SOUTH AMERICA

In June 1834 the Beagle passed through the straits of Magellan to the Pacific Ocean and the west coast of America. They sailed first to Chiloe – a tropical island with volcanic activity – and surveyed the nearby Chonos Archipelago where Darwin saw three active volcanoes and his first fossilised tree.

Royal Zoological Society of London

The Galapagos tortoises.

On February 20th 1835, whilst ashore near Valdivia, Darwin experienced a severe earthquake: *'I happened to be on shore and was lying down in the wood to rest myself. It came on suddenly and lasted two minutes, but the time appeared much longer. The rocking of the ground was very sensible... there was no difficulty in standing upright, but the motion made me almost giddy... A bad earthquake at once destroys our oldest associations: the earth, the very emblem of solidity, has moved beneath our feet like a thin crust over a fluid; – one second of time has created in the mind a strange idea of insecurity, which hours of reflection would not have produced.'*

Sailing into the harbour at Concepción they found the town devastated; the Beagle crew were told *'that not a house in Concepción or Talcahuano (the port) was standing; that seventy villages were*

destroyed; and that a great wave had almost washed away the ruins of Talcahuano.' What interested Darwin most, however, was the fact that the land surface of the town had been permanently elevated by around one metre whilst thirty miles away, on the island of S. Maria *'Captain Fitzroy found beds of putrid mussel shells still adhering to the rocks, ten feet above*

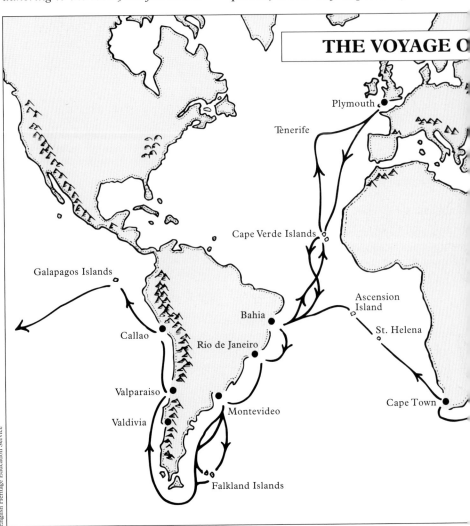

English Heritage Education Service

THE VOYAGE O

Plymouth

Tenerife

Cape Verde Islands

Galapagos Islands

Bahia

Ascension Island

St. Helena

Callao

Rio de Janeiro

Valparaiso

Cape Town

Valdivia

Montevideo

Falkland Islands

high-water mark. The inhabitants had formerly dived at low-water spring-tides for these shells.' It was this earthquake that finally persuaded Darwin to take up the view of the geologist Charles Lyell, that land elevations and subsidences were due to the cumulative effects of physical processes still occurring today such as earthquakes and erosion, rather than the result of some catastrophe.

In April 1835, whilst in Valparaiso, Darwin went on a trek into the Andes to Mendoza, hoping to find evidence of geo

logical uplift. The geology delighted him; he found fossil shells at an elevation of 12,000 feet and he was convinced that the whole mountain range was formed during the tertiary period by the action of earthquakes. Writing to his sister Susan about the age of the mountains, he said:

'If this result shall be considered as proved, it is a very important fact in the theory of the formation of the world. Because if such wonderful changes have taken place so recently in the crust of the globe, there can be no reason for supposing former epochs of excessive violence.'

THE GALAPAGOS ISLANDS

Sailing via Lima, the Beagle arrived, in September 1835, at the Galapagos Archipelago, a group of ten islands formed of volcanic rock. Darwin recorded in his Journal:

'Nothing could be less inviting than

the first appearance. A broken field of black basaltic lava, thrown into the most rugged waves and crossed by great fissures, is everywhere covered by stunted, sunburnt brushwood, which shows little sign of life.'

Everywhere there was evidence of recent volcanic activity; for Darwin this explained the origin of new land, gradually accumulating and rising up from the sea floor.

he was actually visiting the islands. His collection of finches was incomplete and details of the individual islands from which the specimens came were left unrecorded.

AUSTRALIA

Having visited Tahiti and New Zealand, the Beagle arrived in Sydney in January 1836. Darwin

death seems to pursue the aboriginal. We may look to the wide extent of the Americas, Polynesia, The Cape of Good Hope, and Australia, and we find the same result.'

Although he came across little wildlife he did get a chance to examine a rat kangaroo, his first marsupial, and he began to think about the strange character of the Australian species compared to those of the rest of the world.

THE KEELING/ COCOS ISLANDS

Leaving Australia, the ship set off across the Pacific, reaching the Indian Ocean and the Keeling or Cocos Islands in April 1836. This was Darwin's first experience of a coral atoll – a circular coral reef surrounding a shallow lagoon. Darwin had been contemplating their origin long before examining one firsthand; as South America was undergoing gradual elevation he reasoned that the land lying under the South Seas might be undergoing a compensatory subsidence. As an island sank, the encircling corals needing shallow water and light would gradually build upwards to the surface forming a fringe. Eventually, when the island disappeared below the surface, the coral reef, which is dead at the bottom and alive at the top, would surround a shallow lagoon – an atoll. In his journal of researches Darwin describes three type of coral reef – barrier reefs, fringing reefs and atolls: *'we see in each barrier-reef a proof that the land there has subsided, and in each atoll a monument over an island now lost. We may thus… gain some insight into the great system by which the surface of the globe has been broken up, and land and water interchanged.'*

Leaving the Indian Ocean the Beagle set sail for home via Mauritius, the Cape of Good Hope, and St Helena returning to Bahia in Brazil to complete the chronometric observations. The Beagle arrived back in Falmouth on 2nd October 1836, and Darwin left the ship immediately to visit his family.

IE BEAGLE

Cocos Keeling Islands

Mauritius

King George's Sound

Hobart

Sydney

New Zealand

Darwin was particularly interested in the different and very unusual wildlife of the islands – the turtles, giant tortoises, sea iguanas, penguins and seals living in the cold water brought to the tropics from the Antarctic in the Humboldt Current. He also noted the unusually tame birds such as mockingbirds and finches. The finches have since been used to symbolise the islands' influence on Darwin's thoughts on evolution (see page 47). However, Darwin only recognised their significance over the following years, not whilst

was not prepared for the wealth and ostentation of the place:
'…it is a most magnificent testimony to the power of the British Nation. Here in a less promising country, scores of years have done many times more than an equal number of centuries have effected in South America. My first feeling was to congratulate myself that I was born an Englishman.'
Trekking into the interior he met aborigines and reflected on the fact that European colonisation seemed to be killing the native inhabitants: *'Wherever the European has trod,*

INTO THE UNKNOWN

1	2	3	4	5	6	7	8	9	10
11	12	13	14	15	16	17	18	19	20
21	22	23	24	25	26	27	28	29	30
31	32	33	34	35	36	37	38	39	40
41	42	43	44	45	46	47	48	49	50
51	52	53	54	55	56	57	58	59	60
61	62	63	64	65	66	67	68	69	70
71	72	73	74	75	76	77	78	79	80
81	82	83	84	85	86	87	88	89	90
91	92	93	94	95	96	97	98	99	100

Photocopy this page and the blank boxes opposite and enlarge to A3 (141% zoom setting)

| You are unable to land – lose 1 throw | Winds against you – go back 2 spaces | Sickness on board – lose 1 throw | Favourable winds – go on 2 spaces | Crossing the equator – 1 extra throw | Volcanic activity – lose 1 throw | Good place to collect specimens – go on 1 space | Darwin makes interesting discovery – 2 extra throws |

English Heritage Education Service

Instructions for making your own board game

■ You will need:
– the information sheet and map showing the Beagle's voyage
– a photocopy of the pictures showing events on the journey and the blank counters
– the blank game board
– scissors, glue and felt-tip pens.

■ Read the description of the voyage carefully, and follow the route on the map. You may want to use some reference books or an atlas to find out more about some of the places Darwin visited.

■ Cut out the pictures showing events on the journey. Eight pictures have already been drawn for you, and there are four blank squares for you to add your own drawings for different events or places.

■ Using the information sheet and map of the journey, decide in which square of the game board you should place each of the event pictures. Make sure you get the events in the right order – look back to the map to check. You must use each of the eight pictures at least once, and you may want to use some more than once. You do not need to have a picture on every square – spread them out!

■ When you have decided on the best position for each picture, stick the pictures on to the game board. Colour them in if you wish.

■ Cut out the blank counters and decorate them with your own design. Decorate the border of the game board with a suitable design. You may want to stick the game board and counters onto stiff card. You could even design your own spinner to use instead of a die.

■ Now think up your own name for your game.

How to play the game

The game is suitable for 2, 3, or 4 players and is played with a die in the same way as snakes and ladders, throwing a 'six' to start. Give each player a different game counter. You will need to refer back to the information sheet at first to check what each picture means!

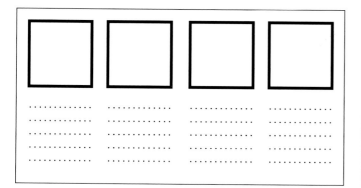

THE BEAGLE'S VOYAGE

Please refer to the map printed on the inside back cover

■ December 1831 – expedition leaves Plymouth

■ Crosses the Bay of Biscay and meets rough seas – Darwin is seasick

■ Unable to land at Madeira as the tides are against them

■ Unable to land at Tenerife as the islanders fear that disease has been carried from Britain

■ Crosses the Atlantic Ocean to Brazil, via the Cap Verde Islands and the equator

■ February 1832 – lands at Bahia (Salvador) in Brazil, where Darwin collects botanical specimens and comes across slavery for the first time

■ On to Rio de Janeiro where Darwin spends two months making observations. He collects 68 species of beetles in one day!

■ Next stop – Tierra del Fuego, and three natives and a Christian missionary are left behind to work with the islanders

■ On to the Falkland Islands where Darwin observes very simple tiny plant-like sea creatures

■ June 1834 – the Beagle sails round the southern point of South America, in the stormy seas of the Straits of Magellan

■ On to the island of Chiloe and the Chonos group of islands, where Darwin observes active volcanoes

■ February 1835 – at Valdivia, Darwin experiences an earthquake, and visits nearby Concepción where he finds the town almost destroyed by the earthquake

■ September 1835 – the Beagle arrives at the Galapagos Islands, where Darwin collects some of his most important specimens, the finches which can only be found on these islands

■ January 1836 – the expedition reaches Australia

■ April 1836 – Darwin observes an atoll, a coral reef around a lagoon, in the Keeling or Cocos Islands

■ The expedition goes round the southern tip of Africa, via the stormy Cape of Good Hope, and crosses the Atlantic to complete work in Brazil

■ October 1836 – the Beagle arrives back at Falmouth and Darwin is reunited with his family

NINETEENTH-CENTURY SHIPS

STEAM POWER

The first steam engines were used to drive ships at the end of the eighteenth century. In 1783, in France the Marquis de Jouffroy d'Abbans built the *Pyrocaphe* which was powered by the new Watt steam engine. Early steamboats were propelled by paddle wheels and in 1807 the paddle steamer, the *Clermont,* steamed the 240 km from New York to Albany in thirty-two hours.

By the second decade of the nineteeth century ships with engines were ocean-going; initially they were not very reliable and coal for fuel was expensive so they also carried sails. Over the century there were several improvements in design.

the space on the ship and made them easier to dock. In the 1860s twin propellers were introduced.

Turbines

In 1894 the British engineer Charles Parsons developed the steam turbine which he fitted to a small 30-metre ship, the *Turbinia.* Using jets of stream from the ship's boilers the turbine drove her up to 60 km an hour, faster than any contemporary steamship.

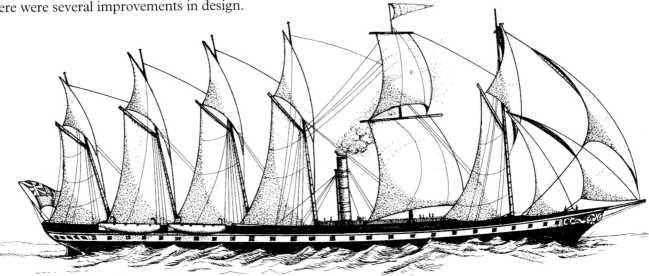

A steamship

STEAM SHIP DESIGN

Paddle steamers

The first steam ships had large round paddles fixed to either side of the boat, partially in the water, which were driven by a steam engine. By turning both paddles together the ship went forwards or backwards; by turning them in opposite directions the ship could turn sharply in either direction.

Propellers

In the 1840s screw propellers were developed and fitted to the sterns of steamships. This development not only increased the speed of the ships, it also made them more stable, it increased

A paddle steamer

SAILING SHIPS

Because steamships had to carry vast quantities of coal as fuel, sailing ships were still used for many long journeys.

Clippers

The clipper ships were built for speed and designed to cut through the water rather than ride it. They had a long narrow, streamlined hull giving the least possible area contact with the water, and originally two, but as speed became crucial, three masts rigged with an exceptionally large spread of sail, and a steel framework for strength and easy maintenance. The first clippers were built for carrying tea from China to London. The first tea of the season commanded the best prices so every year the clippers raced each other back from China non-stop carrying the freshly picked tea to claim the fist prize.

The Beagle

Schooners and brigs

These were all two-masted vessels which, before steam was in general use, were extensively employed in trade from the West Indies, the Baltic and the Mediterranean. Schooners were twenty-five to thirty metres in length and were developed at the beginning of the eighteenth century in the British North American colonies. By the end of the century they had become the most important North American ship for coastal trade and fishing and soon after 1800 were being designed in Europe. They were extensively employed in the fruit trade.

Brigs were slightly larger vessels, twenty-seven to thirty-five metres in length and by the second decade of the nineteenth century brigs were the predominant merchant ship. They were reliable and economic vessels which were simple to build, rig and sail with a small crew. Brigs were also fitted with guns as naval warships. After the Napoleonic wars, however, was a time of peace and the 10-gun brig, of which class the *Beagle* is an example, was used for the exploratory work of the Hydrographic Service and also the mail packet service operated by the navy, running between Falmouth and Halifax, Nova Scotia and around the Mediterranean.

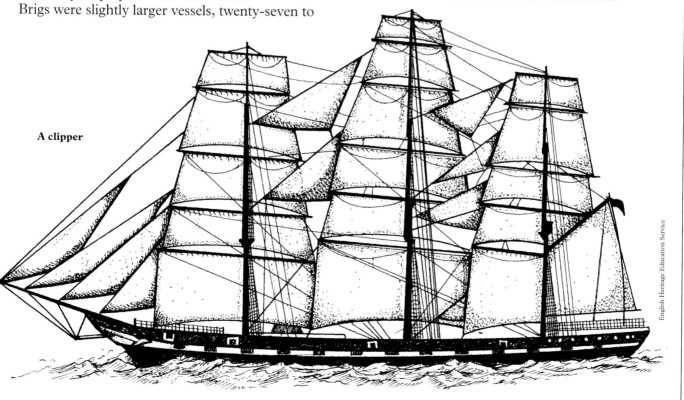

A clipper

MAPPING THE WORLD

Maps and charts are representations of the earth's surface features drawn to scale; cartography is the art and science of making them. One of the important tasks carried out on voyages such as that undertaken by the *Beagle* was to gather accurate information and measurements for map-making.

Topographic maps – these are representations of the natural and man-made features. They show the shape of the land, record elevations above sea level, features such as lakes and rivers as well as roads and settlements.

Nautical charts – these are maps of coastal and marine areas which provide navigational information such as sea depths, channel markers, islands, rocks, reefs and significant features of the coast.

equator. It is the angle, measured in degrees, minutes and seconds, formed at the centre of the earth between a line from the centre to a point on the equator and from the centre to any other point, measured polewards. Thus, the equator is 0° and the North and South Poles 90°.

Latitude could be measured by using a sextant, an instrument developed in the mid-eighteenth century from earlier devices. It combined an arrangement of mirrors, a telescope and a scale and could measure latitude by establishing the angle between the horizon and a celestial body such as the sun, moon or star.

Longitude is the measurement east or west of the Prime Meridian of 0° which passes through both Poles and Greenwich, London. It is measured in degrees, minutes

of the earth at 180° is the International Date Line.

Until nautical almanacs and accurate timepieces called chronometers were developed in the late eighteenth century, it was virtually impossible to determine exact longitude. In 1772 John Harrison designed and constructed a timepiece which was sufficiently accurate to allow longitude to be established by comparing local time with the time at Greenwich.

Triangulation – When a large area is to be mapped it is necessary to know the exact relative positions of a series of points; one method of doing this is by triangulation, a technique first used by the sixteenth-century Bavarian, Philip Apian. It is a means of finding out the position of different places by joining them

The position of a place on the earth's surface is measured by its latitude and longitude. Latitude and longitude are measured in angles not kilometres.

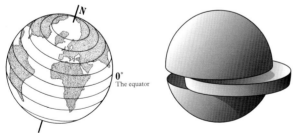
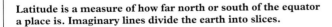

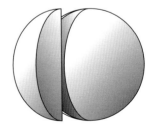

Latitude is a measure of how far north or south of the equator a place is. Imaginary lines divide the earth into slices.

Longitude is a measure of how far round the earth a place is (starting from 0° in Greenwich, and going east or west). Imaginary lines divide the earth into segments.

To make any map the location must be pinpointed on the earth's surface using the imaginary grid of lines of latitude (parallels) and longitude (meridians).

Latitude is measurement of a location north or south of the

and seconds and is the angle created by drawing a line from the centre of the earth to the intersection of the Prime Meridian and the equator and then another from the centre to any other point on the equator. The line opposite the Prime Meridian on the other side

up to form imaginary triangles and measuring the angles between them. If the length of one side of the triangle (the base line) is known and the angles to the other points are accurately measured, the lengths of the other two sides can be worked out.

Nineteenth-century map making

The nineteenth century saw a great advance in cartography. Continental coasts were charted, a start was made on the mapping of the interiors of the unexplored continents of Africa and Australia and the polar regions, and national surveys produced topographical maps of Europe and countries under European influence.

New land mapping

Most of the maps produced from travelling over new terrain were produced by the explorers and were little more than route maps based on distances and bearings; detail depended upon the skill of the surveyors – the distances were tied into observations of latitude and if the surveyors were skilled and had chronometers, also with longitude.

Coastal mapping

After the end of the Napoleonic Wars in 1815 there was a vast expansion in world sea trade. Between 1808 and 1860 the work of the Hydrographic Office of the Royal Navy in charting the coasts, rivers and harbours around the world, vastly increased. Major expeditions were sent to survey Africa, India, South America, Australia and the Pacific islands and the maps became authoritative maps for those areas, in some cases for a hundred years. As well as surveying the coastlines the other major task for the Hydrographic survey was to establish exact positions by latitude and longitude, as existing maps contained many errors.

National surveys

In many European countries national survey organisations were established to carry out standard series of topographical maps. In Britain the Ordnance Survey was officially set up in 1791 and initially had two purposes – the

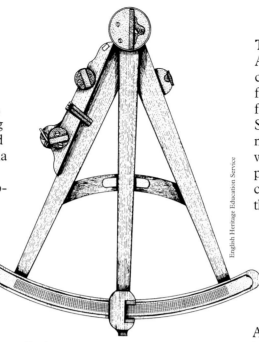

In the 1730s the octant was invented. This enabled navigators to measure the altitude of the sun, moon or stars so they could find their latitude.

carrying out of the great triangulation between 1798 and 1853 and the production of the one inch to one mile map. The first sheet of this was produced in 1801 but it was not until 1870 that it covered the whole of Great Britain.

Thematic maps

At the beginning of the nineteenth century maps began to be used for specialist purposes, especially for the study of geology. William Smith initiated the geological mapping of England and Wales with fifteen sheets engraved and published in 1815 with hand coloured geological data. In 1835 the Geological Survey was established using the Ordnance Survey one-inch sheets as a base. Other maps included Karl Ritter's maps of Europe which showed the inter-relation of relief, vegetation and human activity, and Alexander von Humboldt's isotherm (lines of equal temperature) map showing the geographical and altitudinal limits of plants. Around the middle of the century there was an interest in statistical mapping – population density shown by graded shading, populations of towns shown by proportional circles, and the volumes of traffic shown by flow lines.

TRIANGULATION

Your pupils can apply some of the techniques of triangulation to a mapping exercise at school. A knowledge of angles and how to calculate scale will be needed. The exercise involves having three measurements in order to produce a triangle. One of these measurements is the baseline, here shown as AB. The distance of C is measured from A and B with a tape measure. On the plan AB is drawn to scale, and using compasses with the arcs of the scaled measurements of AC and BC the rest of the triangle can be constructed.

This method differs from that used by mapmakers in that the third point of the triangle is often a distant and inaccessible point. In this case surveying instru-

ments are used to calculate the angles between the points A and B on the baseline and point C. Knowing the length of the baseline and the measurements of these two angles enables the surveyor to construct the whole triangle to scale on paper.

THE OUTCOMES OF THE VOYAGE

THE JOURNAL

'During some part of the day I wrote my journal, and took such pains in describing carefully and vividly all that I had seen; and this was good practice. My journal served, also, in part as letters to my home, and portions were sent to England, whenever there was an opportunity.'

Darwin's journal provides a vivid account of the Beagle voyage

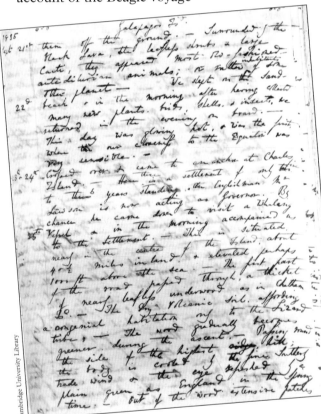

An extract from Darwin's journal.

with descriptions of the countries visited including amongst other things, descriptions of the geology, topography, wildlife and inhabitants. *The Journal of Researches into the geology and natural history of the countries visited during the voyage of HMS Beagle,* (published in 1839) is still in print today and is Darwin's second most reprinted book after *Origin.*

The *Journal* made Darwin famous and in the main it attracted favourable reviews. He was described as a *'first-rate landscape-painter with a pen'* and a *'strong intellectual man and an acute and deep observer'.* Only an anonymous article in the *Athenaeum* was critical, saying his geological theories were too speculative and were based on inadequate facts.

Darwin's advice was sought for natural history collections, geological expeditions and in drawing up recommendations for other research projects. His Journal was one of the recommended texts for the scientists on Sir James Clark Ross's naval expedition to the Antarctic. In 1845 a new edition was published. Darwin extensively revised his original text to make it both of more popular interest and to emphasise the aspects, such as the Galapagos finches, which had since become important for his theories. The journal is therefore in parts a product of hindsight.

THE COLLECTIONS

'Another of my occupations was collecting animals of all classes, briefly describing and roughly dissecting many of the marine ones…'.

Whilst on the Beagle, Darwin amassed a vast collection of specimens many of which he shipped back to Henslow at various stages of the voyage. These consignments, of which there were eight in total, contained anything from corpses, skins, and fossils, to pickled fish, beetles, seeds and rocks, though he tended to focus on the small and seemingly insignificant creatures such as insects, birds, small mammals, reptiles and fish, spiders, corals and barnacles. He wrote from Maldonado, near Montevideo:

'I collect reptiles, small quadrupeds, & fishes industriously, especially the first: The invertebrate marine animals, are however my delight'.

Whilst in Maldonado alone he collected examples of eighty kinds of birds. Fitzroy was amused by the *'cargoes of apparent rubbish'* being brought on board and Wickham complained about him *'bringing more dirt on board than any ten men'* He recorded his specimens in sets of notebooks giving each a number as it was put in the bottle, and a short description noting any exceptional characteristics. As he wrote in the first edition of his journal:

'Let the collector's motto be 'trust nothing to memory', for the memory becomes a fickle

Beetles and beetle fragments belonging to Darwin.

EDUCATIONAL APPROACHES

Sorting into groups

■ Collect pictures of a wide variety of living things. Twenty to thirty examples would be a good number. Try to include examples of insects, reptiles, different types of plants, trees, invertebrates etc. Ask your pupils, working in small groups, to think about sorting them into sets, choosing their own classifications to distinguish between the groups.

■ A good starting point is to divide the items into those that move and those that do not – that is, plants and animals. These two main groups can then be broken down further using criteria suggested by the pupils themselves. They could use
– shape
– where they live (land or water)
– how they feed
– colour
– with or without legs.

This is the process that Darwin had to follow when classifying and cataloguing the vast amount of specimen material he collected on the voyage.

■ Pupils could then make, classify and display their own collections either from their own gardens or the school grounds, having first discussed where it is appropriate to look for these items and which it might not be suitable to collect or pick. Conservation of the natural environment should be an over-riding consideration. Animals or insects which cannot be collected should be described and photographed in their own habitat. Emphasise the importance of careful record-keeping, with details of when and where the item was found, a clear description of it and a drawn or photographic record.

■ Using a large scale (six inches to one mile, or 1:10 000) Ordnance Survey map of the local area, pupils could map their finds, cross-referencing to their object displays and written records.

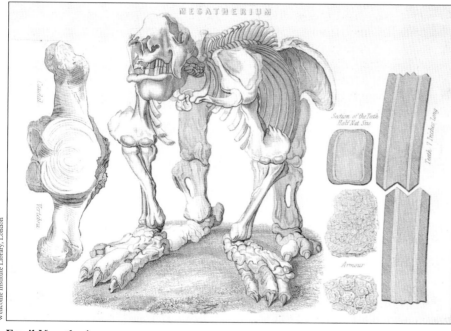

MEGATHERIUM

Fossil Megatherium

guardian when one's interesting object is succeeded by another still more interesting… put a number on every specimen, and every fragment of a specimen; and during the very same minute let it be entered in the catalogue.'

It was not just living species that Darwin collected; he also came across fossil bones of species which seemed to have become extinct in the recent geological past. Amongst other things he found the remains of a giant ground sloth Megatherium, fossil armadillos and a giant rodent Toxodon.

Back in England, Darwin edited the descriptions of his zoological collections which were written up by more experienced naturalists such as John Gould and Richard Owen. *The Zoology of the voyage of HMS Beagle* was published in five parts between 1838 and 1843.

GEOLOGY

To Darwin the study of the geology of an area was of prime importance, as he wrote in a letter to Henslow in May 1832 from Rio de Janeiro, *'Geology & the invertebrate animals will be my chief object of pursuit through the whole voyage'.* He went on board armed with the first volume of Charles Lyell's *Principles of Geology*, which expounded the view that the world was constantly and gradually changing, the past no more violently than the present. Therefore the natural processes occurring in the present such as the erosion, earth movements, volcanic activity etc., were all that was needed to explain the past. By the end of the voyage Darwin described himself as a *'zealous disciple of Mr Lyell's views as known in his admirable book'* and he knew that he would be making a serious contribution to geological debate. Indeed, while Darwin was on the Beagle, the geologist Adam Sedgwick had read some of Darwin's letters to Henslow to the Geological Society in London, and Darwin's observations had stirred up much excitement. On his return, it was his geological publications on the Andes and coral reefs which established his reputation with the scientific elite. His *Structure and Distribution of Coral Reefs* was published in 1842, *Geological Observations on the Volcanic Islands Visited during the Voyage of HMS Beagle* in 1844 and *Geological Observations on South America* in 1846.

CONTEMPORARY EXPEDITIONS

By the beginning of the nineteenth century features of Europe, Asia, North Africa, North and South America and the Pacific islands were largely known. The aims of expeditions contemporary with the Beagle voyage were, therefore:

■ exploratory into the unknown polar regions and continental interiors

■ navigational to chart the coastal waters

■ scientific discovery, the thirst for new knowledge and adventure

■ missionary expeditions by Europeans and Americans who felt it their duty to 'civilise' native populations by transplanting their own languages, laws and religious beliefs.

THE POLAR REGIONS

Interest in the Arctic was largely geographic and scientific – to reach the remotest parts of the earth. With the incentive of a government reward of £20,000 a number of expeditions set out in the nineteenth century in search of the North-West passage, but all were defeated by the ice. It was not until 1906 that the Norwegian sailor, Roald Amundsen, finally conquered the North-West passage.

The Antarctic was also being explored. In 1819 two Russian vessels under the command of Baron Fabian von Bellinghausen set off carrying 100 men, and stores, to the Antarctic. He sailed round the coast of Antarctica until he reached what is now the Bellinghausen Sea. Whilst travelling he made careful and accurate charts and ascertained that the south pole was in fact in the middle of a vast, deserted, and frozen continent – Antarctica. In the years that followed many expeditions were made to the Antarctic, including that of the British Rear Admiral James Clark Ross between 1838 and 1843 who explored a vast area on his ships the *Erebus* and *Terror* and reached the 'Great Ice Barrier'.

THE CONTINENTAL INTERIORS
Africa

At the beginning of the nineteenth century the interior of Africa or 'the dark continent' was largely unexplored. The Scottish surgeon Mungo Park was asked by the African Association of London (later the Royal Geographical Society) to explore the River Niger, known to exist somewhere in north-west Africa; he was drowned on his second expedition attempting to follow its course to the mouth. This was later achieved by the explorer Richard Lander in 1830.

The Scottish missionary-explorer David Livingstone explored much of south central Africa. Sent at first by the London Missionary Society to expose the slave trade he came across Lake Ngami, the formerly unknown Zambezi river, and the falls which the Africans called 'mosioa-tunya' ('smoke thunders there') which he renamed the Victoria Falls.

In 1857 the Royal Geographic Society sent an expedition, led by John Speke and Richard Burton, from the east coast of Africa to explore the central lakes. When Burton fell ill Speke continued alone, and was the first European to discover Lake Tanganyika (which he named Lake Victoria) and later confirmed it to be the source of the Nile.

South America

At the beginning of the century Alexander von Humboldt and Aimé Bonpland travelled through South America studying the geology and collecting plants, and in 1848 Alfred Russel Wallace and Henry Bates set off there. Bates had introduced Wallace to the subject of entomology, and the latter suggested a specimen-collecting trip to the tropical jungles. Wallace spent four years collecting insects in the Amazon basin but his specimens were lost when his ship sank on the return to England. He went on to develop a theory of evolution by natural selection independently of Darwin (see page 56). Bates stayed in South America for eleven years working his way up the Amazon. He collected 14,712 species, mainly insects, around 8,000 of which were new and he kept meticulous records.

Australia

Compared with Africa, relatively little interest was taken in Australia and exploration was slow. Over the course of the first half of the nineteenth century Australian explorers went inland, discovering the vast extent of the country and that the heart of the country was not an inland sea, as had been thought, but a desert.

THE PACIFIC

Exploration in the Pacific was not only a quest for geographical and scientific knowledge. Motives were also financial – procuring whales and seals, establishing trade with China and claiming territory. Between 1838 and 1842 Charles Wilkes led the great United States Exploring Expedition, primarily for naval navigation and charting but also for scientific work. Most of the work was to determine the precise locations of hundreds of islands, reefs and harbours which resulted in the production of 241 charts which remained in use throughout World War II.

THEORIES OF EVOLUTION BEFORE DARWIN

Although Darwin made popular the theory of evolution and proposed the mechanism by which it occurs – natural selection – he was not the first to consider the concept. The French naturalist Georges Buffon (1707-1778) had realised that the earth was far older than had been thought and suggested that living things had probably undergone much alteration. The poet and botanist Johann Goethe (1749-1832) had also published ideas about the evolution of plants, as had Darwin's grandfather, Erasmus (see page 11).

JEAN BAPTISTE DE LAMARCK

Jean Baptiste de Lamarck also proposed a theory of evolution. He amended the ancient doctrine of the 'Great Chain of Being' whereby all species were arranged on an orderly ladder. At the bottom were simple plants followed by fish, reptiles, birds and mammals. Man was about half way up, above were angels and, at the top, God. This arrangement fitted in with the social structure of the eighteenth century. It explained the inequalities of man and everyone knew their place in society. Lamarck's theory, however, had two further elements:

■ the order was not static, but an upward progression with all living things inherently striving to become more complex and to reach higher stages of development. And, as creatures progressed, new organisms arose by 'spontaneous generation'.

■ a second force was at work – the need for creatures to adapt to the local environment. Wading birds developed longer legs to keep

Jean Baptiste de Lamarck

their bodies above water, and snails with poor vision developed feelers. Once these characteristics were acquired, Lamarck believed that they would be passed on to the next generation.

Although the latter idea is now known not to happen, this was the most important evolutionary theory until Darwin put forward his ideas.

UNIFORMITARIANISM

By the end of the eighteenth century thoughts were beginning to change as people began to be aware that the earth was subject to natural laws. The notion of Uniformitarianism was that, instead of the world having been shaped by a series of catastrophes, it had been and was still being shaped very gradually by the ongoing natural processes of erosion, deposition and tectonic activity. This idea was first put forward by the Scottish geologist James Hutton in the eighteenth century but it was not until the nineteenth century that it was popularised by Charles Lyell. This idea of continuous geological change laid the foundations for the theory of continuous biological change.

THE 'VESTIGES OF CREATION'

As the public awareness in fossils was increasing, a pro-evolution pamphlet entitled *The Vestiges of the Natural History of Creation* was published anonymously in 1844. This suggested that the succession of fossil types indicated an increasing transformation of species according to natural laws rather than a sudden creation. The book was the first widely-read book putting forward evolution and

Sir Charles Lyell

caused an outcry; it was scorned by most established naturalists but became an instant success with the public, going through eleven editions by 1860. The speculation of the identity of 'Mr Vestiges' became a popular topic of conversation with suggestions of Charles Lyell, Countess Lovelace – Lord Byron's daughter – and even Prince Albert. It was in fact written by the popular Scottish author Robert Chambers whose other works were reference books and encyclopaedias. His identity was not revealed officially until after his death though many had guessed within a few years of the publication.

DARWIN'S THEORY OF EVOLUTION

The eighteen months following Darwin's return to England were critical in drawing together the evidence from the Beagle voyage and forming his theory of evolution, the stirrings of which he had begun to feel on the final leg of his journey. He had already been converted to Lyell's uniformitarian view and began to realise that if the world had undergone such change,

were similarities between words in Greek, Latin and Sanskrit, and in 1816 a theory by Franz Bopp proposed that all European languages were modifications of a common Indo-European language.

To support his theory Darwin used living and fossil evidence and geographical distribution.

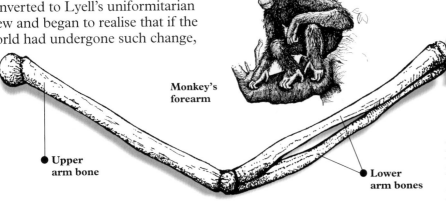

Monkey's forearm

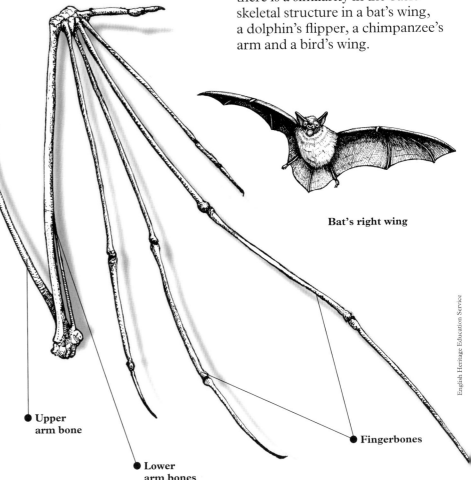

● Wristbones

● Fingerbones

● Upper arm bone

● Lower arm bones

Living evidence
Darwin showed how the same basic pattern of bones appear in the limbs of all mammals each adapted for its own purpose – for example there is a similarity in the basic skeletal structure in a bat's wing, a dolphin's flipper, a chimpanzee's arm and a bird's wing.

species too must have been transformed to adapt. Either they were specially created to replace those lost through extinction or they had evolved from predecessors. He rejected the first explanation and by mid-1837 he was convinced that life had evolved. In July of that year he started a series of notebooks on the 'transmutation of species' filled with his speculations about evolution and the origin of species.

Darwin accepted Lamarck's notion of adaptation but rejected his idea of spontaneous generation on account of evolution not being a single line of ascent. Instead he proposed a branched one with each new species forming a new shoot from the parent branch which led back to a common ancestor. The theory of a common ancestor was not a new one; both Lamarck and Erasmus Darwin had speculated on it and a similar principle had already been applied to linguistics. At the end of the eighteenth century Sir William Jones had demonstrated that there

Bat's right wing

● Upper arm bone

● Lower arm bones

● Fingerbones

English Heritage Education Service

Fossil evidence

Darwin showed that fossils show a gradual succession of changes from reptile to mammal. The *procynosuchus* for example shows some characteristics of a reptile such as a lower jaw comprising several bones, yet has only one row of teeth of different types characteristic of a mammal. He also showed that there were great similarities between living creatures and fossils, for example the *Glyptodon* and modern armadillos in South America.

Geographical distribution

Using islands as an example, Darwin showed that migration and evolution better explained the distribution of plants and animals than did the idea of a 'special creation' of species specifically for islands. The species on the Galapagos Islands had arrived there by various means and had diversified into different forms.

Darwin pointed out similarities in the bone structures of many mammals.

The anatomical drawings on these two pages were based on illustrations from the Dorling Kindersley Eyewitness book *Evolution*.

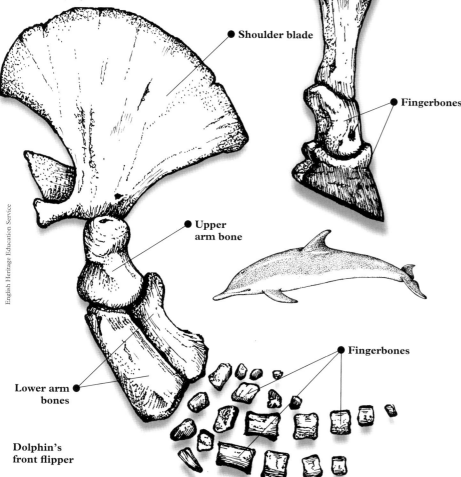

Horse's foreleg

● Handbone

● Shoulder blade

● Fingerbones

● Upper arm bone

● Fingerbones

Lower arm bones

Dolphin's front flipper

HOW NEW SPECIES EMERGE
Species

A species is a group of similar plants or animals which are able to breed successfully together. New species are able to evolve when existing species are separated into groups. Certain environments will favour certain characteristics, thus after generations of breeding the original groups will be so different that they will no longer be able to interbreed. Occasionally, different species can breed together but their offspring is usually sterile. For example, a mule is produced by the interbreeding of a horse and a donkey, but mules cannot breed with each other to produce offspring like themselves.

To illustrate his ideas on species, Darwin used the example of the wildlife of the Galapagos Islands.

Although he did not realise it whilst visiting the islands, he later

Horse

Donkey

Mule

English Heritage Education Service

47

Several of the different kinds of finches Darwin discovered on the Galapagos Islands. Seed-eating finches have big, powerful beaks and insect-eating finches have thinner, pointed beaks.

A Galapagos tortoise

A diagram from Darwin's notebook, to illustrate branching evolution.

recognised that there were thirteen species of finch on the different islands, each with different beaks adapted to obtain their food – some for picking insects from tree trunks, some for poking into cracks, some for crushing seeds, and some for eating buds and leaves. Owing to the strong ocean currents, these geologically recent islands have remained isolated from each other since their formation and have thus all developed slightly different environments. The finches, which probably all evolved from one species which arrived by chance from the South American main-land, have each adapted a suitable beak to survive in their specific habitat. The same process of evolution probably occurred with the different species of Galapagos tortoise.

Darwin proposed that sexual reproduction gave rise to small variations between individuals – offspring not only differed from their parents but also from one another. These random variations could be passed on from one generation to the next. Those changes which were beneficial could eventually lead to permanent changes in form and habit.

ARTIFICIAL SELECTION

By studying artificial breeds of plants and animals developed by gardeners, farmers and stock breeders, Darwin began to realise that the development of new strains was the result of selective breeding or 'artificial selection'. By crossing two individuals with a certain feature, and then crossing the off-spring which also show that feature and so on over several generations, the particular feature will become more and more pronounced.

Darwin recognised that considerable variations had occurred through selective breeding over the previous 50 years and deduced from this the great changes which would have been possible over millennia. His pigeon experiments (see page 51) led him to the conclusion that all varieties of pigeon were ultimately descended from the wild rock dove and he rightly suspected that all breeds of domestic animals such as sheep, horses and dogs were each descended from a single ancestor. DNA tests today have shown that all breeds of dog, for example, are descended from the European wolf.

NATURAL SELECTION

The process of artificial selection necessarily involved choice on the part of the breeder. Darwin recognised that a similar process must occur in nature. In 1838 he read the economist Thomas Malthus' *Essay on the Principle of Population* published in 1798. Malthus had pointed out that all living things tended to increase faster than the increase of food

Thomas Malthus

supply. In humans, if population went unchecked, it would soon outstrip resources, creating a struggle for existence. Poverty, starvation, disease and war were therefore necessary to the existence of society as checks on population, and any attempt to alleviate them would eventually exacerbate suffering. Darwin realised that, where a breeder

made the choice in artificial selection, in nature, when far more offspring than could possibly survive were produced, competition or the 'struggle for existence' played that role.

Peppered moths are camouflaged to merge in to the background.

Scientists already knew that there was competition between different species but Darwin realised there was also competition between individuals of the same species. This competition or 'natural selection' made sense of all his earlier observations and directed the process of evolution; the struggle for existence eliminated the unfit and gave an individual with a favourable feature an advantage in the struggle. This individual might therefore live longer to be able to pass on this variation to the next generation. After hundreds of generations the tiny changes may add up to a significant difference producing adaptation and new species.

A recent example of this adaptation is the case of the peppered moths in Britain. During the industrialisation of the nineteenth century the trees on which the peppered moths rested in the daytime were blackened as pol-

lution killed the light coloured lichens. The light-coloured moths therefore lost their camouflage and could be picked off by predatory birds. The black moths, however, now had the favourable characteristic, were less visible, and therefore had a better chance of survival to be able to pass on their characteristics to the next generation. The number of black moths therefore increased over the generations, adapting to the different surroundings. Since the 1950s, pollution has reduced and the number of light moths is increasing again.

By the end of 1838 Darwin had formulated his hypothesis:

■ the world had undergone and was undergoing continuous transformation, thus life must change in order to survive;

■ nature provides an unlimited supply of hereditary random variations;

■ the fertility of nature means there is always a struggle for existence. Those with favourable characteristics will survive, those without or with unfavourable ones will perish.

SEXUAL SELECTION

As well as natural selection, Darwin also identified the mechanism of sexual selection – the struggle between individuals of the same sex within a species to attract a mate. In some cases this involves fighting between males:

'Male alligators have been described as fighting, bellowing and whirling round like Indians in a war-dance for the possession of the females; male salmon have been observed fighting all day long, male stag-beetles sometimes bear wounds from the huge mandibles of other males; the males of certain hymenopterous insects have frequently been seen ... fighting for a particular female, who sits by, an apparently unconcerned beholder of the struggle, and then retires with the conqueror.'

In other cases it may involve attracting the female; this is especially the case with birds, for example peacocks or birds-of-

paradise, when the males display their bright plumage.
Darwin wrote:

'Thus when the males and females of any animal have the same general habits of life, but differ in structure, colour or ornament, such differences have been mainly caused by sexual selection: that is, by individual males having had in successive generations, some slight advantage over other males, in their weapons, means of defence, or charms, which they have transmitted to their male offspring alone.'

EDUCATIONAL APPROACHES

Similar but different

To show variation between individuals and that everyone is unique – divide the class into boys and girls. Then continue dividing each resulting group on the basis of eye colour, skin colour, hair colour, curliness of hair, right/left handedness, attached/detached ear lobes, the ability to curl the tongue. By the end of this everyone should be on their own (except identical twins!)

Your pupils could take this further by devising their own 'decision trees', based on variations in appearance. Ask them to draw the faces of four people, or to cut out four different faces from magazines or newspapers.

Ask pupils, working in pairs, to choose one of the faces and to make their own decision trees to identify them. Each question in the decision tree must be answerable by 'yes' or 'no' (see example). Ask pupils to check each other's decision trees. What is the fewest questions you can ask to get the correct answer?

The crowded world

Calculations show that if all offspring, for example of animals or insects, survived to the age where they themselves were able to reproduce, the world would be overrun with creatures.

■ One pair of elephants could, if unchecked, produce 19 million descendants after 700 years.

■ One pair of cockroaches could produce 164 thousand million descendants after only seven months.

■ One pair of spiders could produce 427 thousand million million descendants after seven years.

How many mice?

To calculate how quickly populations will grow, we need to know

■ how old the offspring need to be to reproduce

■ how many offspring are produced at a time

■ how often offspring are produced.

Ask your pupils to work out from the following figures the mouse population after six months if all were to survive, (they will have to assume that 50% of each litter is female). How many after one or even two years?

■ The house mouse is able to reproduce when it is two months old.

■ Each litter can contain 10 or even 12 young.

■ The gestation period (from conception to birth) for the house mouse is about three weeks.

The same principles apply to the plant kingdom. Plants which have many seeds could rapidly overrun the earth if conditions were right and all seedlings survived. For example, after seven years a poppy could have produced 820 thousand million million million descendants.

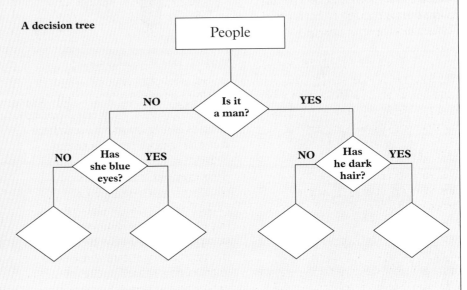

A decision tree

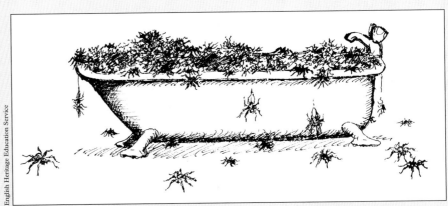

English Heritage Education Service

EXPERIMENTS AT DOWN HOUSE

BARNACLES

Darwin realised that if his theories were to be taken seriously he would have to prove himself a serious scientist. Therefore, in order to show himself capable of detailed biological investigation, he devoted himself to the study of the small marine invertebrates *cirripedia* or barnacles. He was drawn to the study of barnacles after finding, on the coast of Chile, an unusual form that differed so much from all the other barnacles that a new sub-order had to be created for it. In order to examine the new form he dissected, studied and classified the whole group of the common forms of barnacle. This work was such a part of everyday life in Down House that one of his sons is said to have asked a neighbour's child *'Where does your father do his barnacles?'*.

His results were finally published in 1851 to 1854 in *Cirripedia*, a detailed work of two volumes which is still a basic reference work for barnacle specialists today.

PIGEONS

Darwin had been interested in domestication and selective breeding ever since he started his notebooks after the voyage. For years he had studied manuals on pig and poultry breeding and animal husbandry, read the *Poultry Chronicle*, attended agricultural shows, talked with breeders and collected information on exceptional animals both at home and in the colonies. From 1855 he decided he needed to study birds more closely and by the middle of that year pigeons had become his passion. At first he just wanted information; to William Fox in March of that year he wrote *'As you have a Noah's ark, I do not doubt that you have pigeons. Now what I want to know is, at what age nesting pigeons have their tail feathers sufficiently*

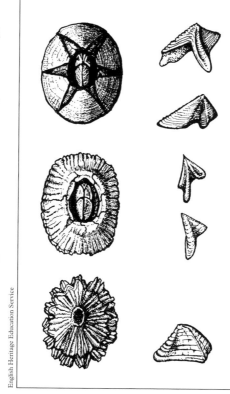

English Heritage Education Service

Darwin spent eight years studying barnacles, marine crustaceans with a hard shell.

developed to be counted. I do not think I ever saw a young pigeon'.

Shortly afterwards he had a pigeon house built and acquired his own ornamental pigeons in order to study the variations between the different breeds – at one point he had sixteen different kinds. Although he did not breed show birds himself, he read widely on the subject, talked endlessly with pigeon fanciers and joined their clubs in order to be able to recognise the minute differences between the birds, invisible to all but the enthusiast. His research into their growth and development led him to demonstrate that they were all descended from a common ancestor, the wild rock dove. Through generations of selective breeding the tiny differences had been accentuated to form the pouters, fantails, runts and tumblers of today – so different

that, had they been wild, they could have been different species.

His enthusiasm for the subject grew. Writing to Charles Lyell in November 1855 he stated *'I am deeply immersed on the subject of Pigeons, & have pairs of seven or eight kinds alive & am watching them outside & then shall skeletonise them & watch their insides'*. Killing the birds however, was a part of the experiment which he did not enjoy. He wrote to Fox *'I am getting quite a 'chamber of horrors' ... I have done the black deed & murdered an angelic little Fan-tail & Pouter at 10 days old.'* Boiling down the carcasses was also extremely unpleasant and in then end he wrote to his friend Thomas Eyton who owned one of the finest collection of skins and skeletons of European birds: *'...will you be so kind as to take the trouble to give me some pieces of information ...when I took the body out of the water, the smell was so dreadful that it made me retch awfully. Now I was told that if I hung the body of a bird or small quadruped up in the air & allowed the flesh to decay off, & the whole to get dry, that I could boil the mummy in caustic soda, & so get it nearly clean, but not white, with very little smell. What do you think of this plan? And pray tell me how do you get the bones moderately clean, when you take the skeleton out, with some small fragments of putrid flesh still adhering? It really is most dreadful work – Lastly do you pluck your birds?'*

In 1856, however, Darwin sent the specimens out to have the skeletons properly prepared.

It was not only the skeletons of birds that he studied but also dogs, rabbits, pigs and fishes, in all cases acquiring information from experts in the subject.

EARTHWORMS

Darwin had a lifelong interest in the humble earthworm, a creature

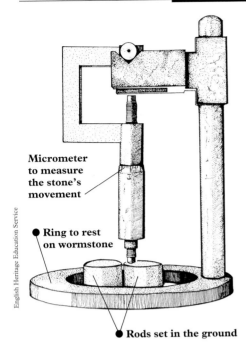

Micrometer to measure the stone's movement

● Ring to rest on wormstone

● Rods set in the ground

Darwin devised a special instrument to help him measure the action of worms in the soil. He placed a millstone on his lawn, with this instrument placed in the middle, to measure how far the stone sank each year.

which had an indirect bearing on plants as it dealt with the production of soil necessary for their growth. By eating earth to obtain the particles of food which it contains, the earthworm grinds it down into a fine powder, and brings it up to the surface, ejecting it as worm-castings.

After his return from the *Beagle* voyage, Darwin was walking at Maer Hall in Staffordshire, the home of his uncle Jos, and noted that lime which had been spread over a field ten years earlier now lay under 2.5 inches (6 cms) of fine mould; it had been covered at a rate of about a quarter of an inch a year. He calculated a similar rate for a field at Downe, over a period of thirty years: *'When [my sons] ran down the slope the stones clattered together. I remember doubting whether I should live to see these larger flints covered with vegetable mould and turf ...[but] after 30 years (1871) a horse could gallop over the compact turf... and not strike a single stone ... the transformation was wonderful [and was] certainly the work of the worms.'* Towards the end of his life, worms became his chief occupation at Down. His son Horace designed a 'wormstone' with a central gauge to calculate the rate at which a stone

sank into the ground; he calculated the rate to be 2.22 mm a year. The wormstone may still be seen in the garden at Down House. He observed how much earth was brought up by the worms and worked out that in every acre of the chalk downland eighteen tons of earth was brought up by earth worms annually.

Darwin turned his billiard room into a study littered with worms and earth in glass covered pots. He experimented with different light sources – candles, paraffin lamps and coloured lanterns but only an intense beam caused them to bolt into their burrows. They seemed to be neither sensitive to heat nor sound – Emma and the children played different instruments or

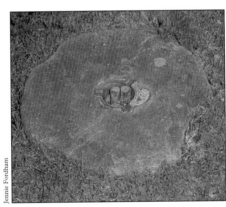

The wormstone at Down House

shouted at them. Breathing on them, however, made them retreat and Darwin tested their sense of smell by exhaling into the pots, chewing tobacco or sucking on scented cotton wool. It seemed that they preferred raw carrots to other vegetables such as celery and cabbage. Darwin also studied their eating habits and their technique of dragging leaves into burrows. He published his *Formation of Vegetable mould, through the action of worms, with observations on their habits* in October 1881 and sold thousands within weeks. Darwin received numerous letters – everyone seemed to have a question or observation to make.

PLANT EXPERIMENTS
Seed dispersal

Darwin, remembering the similarities between the species on the

Galapagos islands and those on the South American mainland, was always interested in the way in which animals and plants were distributed across the globe. Unlike his scientific colleagues who believed that land bridges must once have connected areas now separated by water, Darwin believed that the distribution owed itself to the individual organism's power of dispersion.

Over several years at Down, Darwin carried out experiments in order to investigate this theory further. In order to test whether seeds might survive long journeys in the ocean to be able to germinate on some distant shore, he put seeds from the kitchen garden into tanks and bottles filled with salt water. He kept these in the garden or in a tank of snow in the cellar in case they were affected by cold and, taking a few seeds from each bottle at intervals he would plant them in glass dishes on the mantelpiece in the study to see if they would germinate. Almost everything came up after a week in salt water and vegetables still sprouted after two weeks. He reported his findings in the *Gardeners' Chronicle* – cress, lettuce, carrot and celery had still germinated well after six weeks of salt water immersion. He then calculated that the average current in the Atlantic was thirty three nautical miles a day, therefore over forty two days a seed might travel fourteen hundred miles, in fact from Europe to the Azores. *'The really interesting thing would be to get a list of the Azores plants, & try & get the seeds of as many as I could and test them; & by Jove I will!'* After a while he realised that the seeds in fact sank to the bottom of the tanks and therefore could not have been transported by such means. However, seeds buoyed up by branches and dried seeds could stay afloat for some time, so Darwin turned his attention to carrying out the experiment with dried plants, nuts and fruit. Even these, within a month, were at the bottom of the tank. Darwin went on to look at other dispersal methods, considering, for example, whether seeds were transported by birds either in

This page: Orchids with their variety of markings.

English Heritage Education Service

their digestive system or attached to their feet or feathers. He counted seeds in mud attached to the feet of partridges which he had sent Parslow out to shoot and his son suggested seeing for how long a dead pigeon would float. He conducted the experiment and found that *'a pigeon had floated for 30 days with seeds in crop & they have grown splendidly'*. He analysed owl droppings to see how many undigested seeds which had passed through the bird would germinate.

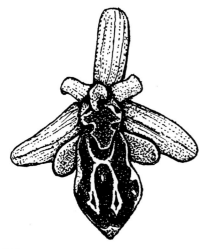

Plant variation and fertilisation

Darwin carried out many experiments on plant variation and hybridisation; he began a series of experiments, crossing more than thirty varieties of garden peas. He noted their increase of sterility. His friend Joseph Hooker at Kew Gardens provided him with contacts to supply seeds and information or, if necessary, sent them direct from the Gardens themselves. Darwin tried growing them in different conditions such as under coloured glass domes or in

over-rich manure; he tried plucking the flowers of plants over several years, and pruning. In a letter to Henslow in June 1855 he wrote:

'I have become very fond of little experiments, & I mean to try whether I cannot break the constitution of plants by coloured glass, picking off flowers, sowing at the wrong time &c &c &c &c in a short time...'

Darwin also became very interested in plant fertilisation. Most botanists at the time believed that plants were self-fertilising, but Darwin's theories of variation required sexual reproduction. Variations in offspring could only

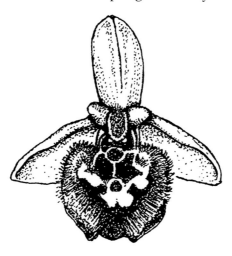

appear through sexual reproduction; with no variations there could be no selection and no transmutation.

To understand the fertilisation process, Darwin spent much time imitating the action of bees landing on plants, with a paintbrush. He studied numerous varieties of plant to show the mutual adaptations of insects and plants which enabled the plants to receive pollen from another flower rather than from itself. In 1861, following a holiday in Torquay where he had spent many hours observing insects visiting wild orchids, Darwin developed a passion for the flower, which was at the time a popular fancy amongst wealthy Victorians. Orchid hunters went out to the tropics to collect prize examples. Darwin made enquiries to these collectors and received a host of rare specimens. He studied the curiously shaped petals which guided the bees and moths to the

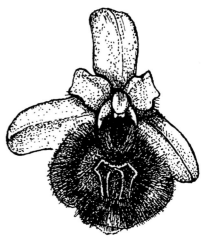

nectaries and the particular spot for receiving pollen which could then be carried to another flower for cross-pollination. He became so

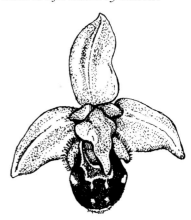

involved with orchids that he had a hot-house built and stocked it with specimens from Kew. Only the bee orchid seemed to be a self-fertiliser and Darwin predicted that is was doomed to extinction. In 1862 he published his work on the subject *The various contrivances by which orchids are fertilised by insects.*

Insectivorous plants

Soon after the publication of *Origin*, Darwin began to take an interest in insectivorous plants such as Venus's flytrap, sundews and pitcher plants:

'During the summer of 1860 I was surprised by finding how large a number of insects were caught by the leaves of the common sundew on a heath in Sussex. I had heard that insects were thus caught but knew nothing further on the subject.'

Having acquired some plants Darwin began his experiments. He studied the movement of the plants when catching prey, the secretion of glands during digestion and the absorption of digested matter. He

EDUCATIONAL APPROACHES

In Darwin's footsteps

Your pupils could carry out simple classroom versions of some of Darwin's experiments.

Earthworms

■ Put layers of soil about six centimetres deep into a glass tank. If possible, use a different colour soil for each layer, or use different types of medium such as growing compost, bulb fibre and a mixture of sand and soil as well as ordinary garden soil. Or use soil with distinctive colours from different areas.

■ Shake each layer so it is even before adding the next. level the top layer gently.

■ Mark on the side of the tank the level of each layer, including the top layer, as accurately as possible.

■ Collect several earthworms, twelve would be a good number, and place them on the surface of the soil.

■ Put the tank in a spot where one side receives a lot of daylight, and shade the other side. Ask your pupils to observe the activity of the worms on a regular basis, daily, weekly, and monthly, keeping careful records of what they see. How long is it before the different layers are no longer clear? How long before the layers are completely mixed? Is there more or less worm activity on the light or shaded side? Has the depth of the soil increased at all?

■ The earthworms will need feeding. Their usual diet is a mixture of leaves and grass. This should be finely chopped before being sprinkled on top of the soil. Your pupils could replicate some of Darwin's experiments by offering them different types of food, such as different fruit and vegetables chopped up, small pieces of cheese or bread or even little pieces of meat. Ask your pupils to record carefully whether any of this food is eaten. The earthworms will need moisture, so keep the top of the soil damp with a water sprayer.

■ Your pupils will need patience for these activities, as Darwin himself spent years studying earthworms. It would be best to start the experiments at the beginning of your topic, to give plenty of time for your pupils' observations.

Growing seeds

Your pupils could carry out germination experiments.

■ First soak different varieties of seeds in jars of salt water for different lengths of time as Darwin did. (Fast germinating seeds such as radish, varieties of cress, and broad beans are best in the classroom for quicker results.)

■ Plant the seeds and note carefully how long they take to germinate. Plant some unsoaked seeds to act as a control for the experiment. How long can a seed be soaked for and still germinate?

■ Keep each plant watered and in good light conditions. After germination is there any difference between the growth rate and health of plants from soaked and unsoaked seeds?

	Not soaked	germinated in	first true leaves	comments
cress				
broad bean				
radish				

	Soaked for	germinated in	first true leaves	comments
cress				
broad bean				
radish				

tested the plants by feeding them with numerous different substances, including saliva, milk, cheese, raw meat, eggs, strychnine, nicotine, alcohol, cobra venom, pen quill and human urine. Another experiment, carried out by Darwin's son, investigated carnivority. With two groups of plants, one was fed with insects, the other left unfed. The insect-fed plant thrived, producing more flowers and seeds. In 1875 Darwin published his fourteenth book – *Insectivorous Plants*.

THE PUBLICATION OF 'ORIGIN' AND CONTROVERSY

Darwin had formulated the basic theory of evolution by natural selection by the early 1840s, but he did not publish it until 1859. This was partly out of scientific caution (he needed to carry out experiments to substantiate his theory), and partly because he was afraid of the storm of controversy which might arise, since his ideas directly challenged Victorian Christianity and the accepted idea of God's creation of the world.

CREATIONISM

According to contemporary Christian and Jewish belief, God created the world, and its form today is the result of His initial design and the damage He inflicted in the great flood. People argued over the date of the creation but most agreed it was a recent event; indeed in the seventeenth century Archbishop James Ussher dated it to 4004 BC. In the flood God ordered Noah to take a pair of every living creature into the ark so none would die out completely and species would remain unchanged.

Since the orthodox Christian belief therefore held that no creature could become extinct, fossils posed a problem. Initially they were regarded as God's ornamental decoration, replicas of living creatures, but once it was established that they were of organic origin, a new explanation was needed. At first it was believed that the creatures must exist in other parts of the world but by the end of the eighteenth century such large fossils had been found that this explanation began to be thought unlikely and the idea of extinction came into play; it was the work of God who had deliberately destroyed his work and recreated it once man had been punished. The

The Christian theory of creation. God creates the birds and fish.

flood therefore explained the shells found in the mountains and the Earth's sedimentary rocks formed from layers of sand and silt deposited during it. Geological discoveries had, however, revealed not a single layer of fossils but many layers. Instead of one flood, therefore, it was believed that there had been a series of catastrophes – earthquakes, climatic changes and floods – the flood at the time of Noah being the last – each time destroying life on Earth, which God then recreated.

Study of the fossils went on to reveal that the nature of the fossils in the different layers was not the

same, invertebrates appear in the lowest levels, then fish, birds, mammals and humans successively higher. This gave rise to the idea of progressionism, that God had intended nature to develop in stages.

Over the eighteenth century, scientists became increasingly aware of the remarkable design of living things. It was impossible that they could have arisen spontaneously; they must have been the work of an intelligent designer-God. One of the most famous arguments for this was that of the 'Watchmaker' put forward by the English clergyman William Paley at the beginning of his *Natural Theology, of Evidences of the Existence and Attributes of the Deity* (1802), a work much admired by Darwin in his theology days at Cambridge. In this, Paley provided an analogy with a watch with moving parts, all designed to work together for a purpose. Just as the existence of a watch proved thre was a watchmaker, so the existence of an animal proved that there was a creator.

PUBLICATION OF 'ORIGIN'

It was these beliefs that Darwin's *On the Origin of Species by means of natural selection, or the preservation of favoured races in the struggle for life*, directly challenged. He worked in secret on his theory in the privacy of Down House for nearly twenty years, telling only a few close friends about his ideas. In early 1856 Charles Lyell urged him to write up an abstract of the theory for publication, in case others did it first. This Darwin started to do but

Alfred Russel Wallace

in June 1858 his plans were overthrown when he received a letter from the naturalist Alfred Russel Wallace enclosing a paper in which he put forward his own theory of natural selection. Wallace knew of Darwin's experimental work and believed him to be working on a large book on 'species and varieties'. Writing many years

later he stated:
'I wrote a letter to him [Darwin] in which I said that I hoped the idea would be as new to him as it was to me, and that I would supply the missing factor to explain the origin of species. I asked him if he thought it sufficiently important to show it to Sir Charles Lyell, who had thought so highly of my former paper.'
The article sent Darwin into a panic *'Your words have come true with a vengeance that I shd be forestalled'* he wrote to Charles Lyell *'...I never saw a more striking coincidence. If Wallace had my M.S. sketch written out in 1842 he could not have made a better short abstract! Even his terms now stand as Heads of my Chapters.... So all my originality, whatever it may amount to, will be smashed.'* Without consulting Wallace, Lyell and Sir Joseph Hooker, two of the country's most eminent scientists and Darwin's confidants, arranged to have some of Darwin's early drafts published alongside Wallace's paper in the journal of the Linnaean Society in 1858. Darwin then went on to work flat out on his *Origin of Species* which he completed just over a year later. It was published on 24 November 1859, whilst Darwin was at a water cure in Ilkley, and the entire print run of 1,250 copies was bought up by book sellers on the first day. Over the next seventeen years it went through six revised editions and is still in print today.

THE RECEPTION OF 'ORIGIN'

Despite Darwin's fears about meeting a wall of opposition, his ideas had been taken up by a small network of influential scientists who openly defended his views; these included:

■ **Joseph Hooker** (1817-1911), the botanist, Darwin's closest friend and confidant who had classified the plant material from the *Beagle* voyage and had tested his hypotheses, collected samples and provided information on plant classification and distribution;

■ **Thomas Henry Huxley** (1825-1895), the zoologist, who

met Darwin in 1856 and was won over by the theory of evolution. On reading *Origin* he remarked *'how extremely stupid not to have thought of that myself'*. He is remembered as 'Darwin's bulldog', the chief spokesman for his ideas;

■ **John Lubbock** (1834-1913) lived three miles from Down House and as a boy was greatly influenced by Darwin. He went on to work in prehistory, establishing glacial periods and coining the terms Palaeolithic and Neolithic.

The main opponents to the publication were the clergy and those scientists with entrenched creationist views because:

■ it was blasphemous, denying God's creation

■ the struggle for survival combined with small, chance variations, took the divine intention out of creation

■ man was supposed to have been created in 'God's image', and not to have apes as ancestors.

One clergyman is reported to have called Darwin *'the most dangerous man in Europe'*, but the clash with the church was most clearly seen at a meeting of the British Association for the Advancement of Science in Oxford in June 1860, when Huxley confronted the Bishop of Oxford, Samuel Wilberforce, known as 'Soapy Sam' in front of a large audience. Wilberforce asked Huxley whether he was descended from an ape on his grandfather or grandmother's side. Huxley retaliated and as Hooker stated *'the battle waxed hot'*. Lubbock and Hooker spoke after Huxley in support of Darwin. Hooker was enraged by Wilberforce and getting on to the platform he launched an attack. He wrote to Darwin of this moment:
'I smashed him amid rounds of applause – I hit him in the wind at the first shot in 10 words taken from his own ugly mouth – & then proceeded to demonstrate in as few more, 1 that he could never have read your book

Thomas Huxley

& 2 that he was absolutely ignorant of the rudiments of Bot[anical] Science....'

Some established scientists with creationist views also could not accept the theory. Darwin's former teacher, the geologist Adam Sedgwick (1785-1873) could not understand his pupil's 'error' and was upset by his efforts to substitute divine creation with natural law. The comparative anatomist Richard Owen (1804-1892), whom Darwin had consulted over the *Beagle* material and who had written up the zoology of the voyage, was partly driven by pride and envy to discredit the theory. Darwin was, however, more concerned about other criticisms.

OBJECTIONS TO DARWIN'S THEORIES

The zoologist H. St George Mivart (1827-1900) embraced the Darwinian theory of evolution but tried to reconcile it with his devout Catholic beliefs by having God intervene in the evolutionary process and introduce a soul. Huxley eventually challenged his views which led Mivart to take an anti-Darwinian stance, one of his main arguments being that natural selection did not explain the initial stages of development of adaptive structure – how for example would the development of an eye or a wing get started – what advantage would

they give without being fully useful? In 1871 he published *On the Genesis of species 'to show that the Darwinian theory is untenable, and that natural selection is not <u>the</u> origin of species… upon scientific grounds only'.*

Darwin countered this with the explanation that the modification may have had a completely different purpose from that of today; the beginnings of wings, for example may have been used for heat regulation.

Samuel Wilberforce, Bishop of Oxford.

Gaps in the fossil record were also used as an argument against Darwin's theory. Darwin was well aware of this but assumed that the intermediate stages had been destroyed and would be recovered by future research. This in fact has not happened and it is now believed that there have been long periods of stability and that all change need not necessarily have been gradual; abrupt transformations may occur.

Geologists were already aware that, for the changes that had taken place on earth to have occurred, an immense length of time was necessary. The physicist William Thomson (later Lord Kelvin) attacked Lyell's uniformitarian geology claiming that since the interior of the earth is hot it must be constantly cooling and thus cannot have been maintained in a steady state for great lengths of time. He calculated that the earth was at

most 100 million years old (he later revised this to 20 million years) a figure which he had based on the rate of heat loss from the Earth. By attacking Uniformitarianism, he also undermined Darwin's theory; the earth was not old enough for all the gradual changes Darwin proposed. Kelvin concluded that God's design was the only explanation for adaptive change. Lord Kelvin was later proved wrong when Pierre Curie discovered that radium salts constantly give out heat thus warming up the earth's crust and counteracting the cooling effect. The earth is now thought to be 4,500 million years old, plenty long enough for evolution.

Another objection to Darwin's theory concerned the mechanism of inheritance. Darwin knew a great deal about the practical side of inheritance, but had no idea how it could take place. In 1867 the Scottish engineer Fleeming Jenkin

Sir Richard Owen. He did his best to discredit Darwin's theory.

suggested that a favourable advantage would be diluted when the individual bred with normal individuals and the variation would be distributed. In a paper published around the same time, Gregor Mendel showed this not to be the case (see page 68) but his work was neglected until 1900.

HUMAN ORIGINS AND VICTORIAN THOUGHT

By the end of the 1860s most botanists and zoologists had accepted the idea of evolution, although the mechanism by which it occurred was still in doubt. Many believed that it was not governed solely by natural law but also required divine or supernatural guidance, especially where humans were concerned. Throughout the 1860s people were upset by the idea that humans might be descended from apes. The traditional view was that the human mind stood above nature. Wallace and Darwin shared views on evolution, and although Wallace was no supporter of orthodox religion, even he believed that the human intellect could only have developed through some supernatural force. After publishing this idea in 1869, Darwin wrote to him 'As you expected I differ grievously from you, and I am very sorry for it. I can see no necessity for calling in an additional and proximate cause in regard to man.' Despite Huxley's *Man's place in nature*, published in 1863, in which he demonstrated that humans were more closely related to apes than apes were to monkeys, he had not actually proved an ape ancestry for humans. Opponents of the theory declared there to be too considerable a gulf between humans and living apes for them to share ancestry. By the end of the decade Darwin saw the necessity to make public his own views.

From the start, he had accepted that man was no more than a highly developed animal but, knowing this to be a highly sensitive issue, had avoided the question of human origins in *The Origin of Species* with the exception of one line 'Light will be thrown on the origin of man and his history'. In his autobiography Darwin wrote that he added this line 'In order that no honourable man should accuse me of concealing my views'.

Wellcome Institute Library, London.

Thomas Huxley, one of Darwin's supporters.

English Heritage Photo Library

Early Bronze Age flint arrowhead.

In 1871 Darwin published what is often considered his second most important work, *The Descent of Man,* in which he discusses his own version of human origins and how the species had acquired superior mental powers.

The first half of the book uses data from embryology, comparative anatomy, behaviour and anthropology to deal with the physical similarities between man and apes – the brain, sense organs, reproduction, gestation, development as well as instinct and emotions. He goes on to the theory that humans and apes diverged from a common ancestor when the human line moved from living in the trees to the plains. Here early hominids adopted an upright posture which freed the hands to make tools, and this was followed by an increase in brain size. Intelligence was thus a result of a shift in lifestyle and the struggle for survival.

THE IDEA OF PROGRESS

By the late 1850s, with the discovery of primitive stone tools and fossils, archaeologists and anthropologists began to accept the antiquity of the human species, and the belief in cultural and social progress was gaining in popularity. Evolution was perceived to be a progressive linear scale with modern industrial civilisation as the ultimate goal to which all races aspired. The modern 'savages' represented a stage through which Europeans had once passed, but due to environmental factors, they were prevented from advancing further up the scale. Anthropologists such as Lubbock believed that not only were 'savages' culturally at a lower level but also mentally – they represented an earlier stage in biological evolution, the link between apes and men. The view that the development of the mind went hand in hand with the development of civilisation was accepted by the Victorians who were eager to find excuses for their conquest of other societies. The non-industrialised societies were thought to be mentally inferior and evolutionary failures, thus their displacement by 'higher' industrialised societies was inevitable.

Despite the fact that Darwin deplored slavery and the harsh treatment of blacks, he nevertheless accepted the widely-held view of white supremacy. He did not question the views of his contemporaries who claimed that the brain capacity and thus intelligence of the whites was greater than any other, and that Europeans were the head of the hierarchy of racial types. Nevertheless he was convinced that all races shared the same ancestry although he could not understand how some of the racial characteristics could be explained in terms of adaptation. He decided the explanation for this was sexual selection – the competition for mates (see page 47).

Darwin dealt with this theory in the second part of *The Descent of Man*. He collected evidence from insects, birds and animals as well as sending questionnaires to missionaries and travellers across the world for information on the idea of beauty among the various native populations. He concluded that non-adaptive characteristics distinguishing different races were the result of different perceptions of beauty. *The Descent of Man* did not cause the storm that *Origin* did since . by the time it was published most had come to terms with the theory of evolution. In relation to humans it fitted in with the fashionable idea of progress, with humans at the top of the evolutionary tree.

SOCIAL DARWINISM

From the 1870s the idea of Darwinism began to be used to support political and economic ideologies. Known as Social Darwinism and based more on the writings of the philosopher Herbert Spencer (1820-1903) who became known for his interest in laissez faire industrial capitalism and who actually coined the phrase 'survival of the fittest', it was particularly popular in America. Proponents of Social Darwinism believed millionaires to be the 'fittest' individuals in society who, according to the American Professor William Graham Sumner (1840-1910), were *'naturally selected in the crucible of competition'*. He argued that the strong were the industrious and frugal; the weak, the idle and extravagant. *'If we do not like survival of the fittest, we have only one possible alternative, and that is the survival of the unfittest. The former is the law of civilization; the latter is the law of anti-civilization.'* By this philosophy the excesses of capitalism were scientifically justified.

Not only was evolutionary theory used to justify capitalism but also at the opposite extreme, communism. Karl Marx believed that it provided ammunition against the divine right of kings and a social hierarchy supported by religion. The idea of continued competitive strife fitted with his ideology of class struggle.

Darwin had not intended his theory to be extended in these ways. Thomas Huxley, a supporter of Darwin's theory, believed that although nature was ruthless, man had the choice not to accept its processes and could struggle for a more compassionate, humane society. Others however believed that man must conform to nature's processes, however ruthless they may be. The theory was taken one step further by Darwin's cousin, Francis Galton (1822-1911) who introduced the idea of 'eugenics'; that mankind had the responsibility and power to improve the human race. He wanted to encourage the most intelligent, fit and moral of society to have large families and to prevent the retarded, feeble and criminally insane from reproducing. '*The first object is to check the birth rate of the unfit ... the second object is the improvement of the race by furthering the productivity of the fit.*' This argument, in its extreme form, was used to justify the sterilisation and mass murder of the 'unfit' in Nazi Germany.

EDUCATIONAL APPROACHES

The ideas contained in this section are sensitive and complex and probably best tackled with older pupils, where useful links could be developed between GCSE history, science and religious studies courses.

Try holding a formal debate with your pupils, based around one of the moral issues raised in the section above. For example, there are often stories in the media about the rights of all people, including those with mental or physical disabilities, to marry and have children.

Propose the statement that all people should be allowed to have children, as a human right that cannot be taken away. Ask two pupils to speak in support of the statement and two to oppose it, and allow time for the speakers and the rest of the class to do some research into the issue. (This stage is essential if the debate is to be more than a statement of personal and unsupported views.)

In preparation for the debate, pupils could find out

■ how the ideas of Darwin and his contemporaries could be used either to support or refute the statement

■ examples of how the ideas of Darwin and his contemporaries have been used to justify actions of governments or individuals this century

■ the practical aspects of support offered to children born to parents with disabilities.

CREATION STORIES

How did the world begin? Where did people come from? These questions have been asked since the beginning of time. All cultures have developed their traditional stories, handed down through the generations, to explain creation. These stories, although very different from one another, often follow a similar pattern with a god or gods creating the heavens and the earth, shaping the land and creating living creatures and mankind. These explanations usually become very important in a society, forming the foundation for many other beliefs and traditions. Questioning the established beliefs about creation, as Darwin's theories did, is often seen as a threat to the whole fabric of that society's structure. Although Darwin's ideas were seen to be contradicting Christian ideas, the following stories show that his views were at odds with many other traditional views on creation.

THE PACIFIC

The Tahitian myth of the creation of the world, variations of which are found through many of the Pacific islands, says that the first God, Ta-aroa, hatched from an incubating egg which existed in empty space. Ta-aroa then created as a companion the God, Tu, and together they made the universe, land, creatures and man. The first man, made from earth, was Ti-i and his wife, half-goddess, half-mortal with a face both in the front and back, was Hina. Hina was full of goodness; Ti-i was the opposite and liked to see others suffer, and so sent out a heron to cast a spell on the world.

After some time the Gods and men started fighting and as a punishment Ta-aroa and Tu sent curses on the world; the moon

Wellcome Institute Library, London.

Sarasvati is a river goddess of the Hindu religion. She is the giver of fertility and wealth, and she is seen here with her sitar and peacock.

faded, the sea fell to low tide, the rivers disappeared into the ground, the leaves fell from the trees and mankind was cursed. Hina, however, manage to save the moon, although it would disappear it would always reappear little by little, there was high tide as well as low tide, waters appeared out of the ground in the form of springs and the tree grew new leaves. Despite all this, Ti-i, supporting Ta-aroa and Tu, used his magic to prevent her saving mankind;

thus it is said that it was man, not woman, who caused mankind to lose eternal life.

HINDU

In the beginning was a dark emptiness, warm and steadily rippling. Gradually the darkness began to make a word, continuously repeating itself; OM ....OM.... and slowly the empty universe was turned into an endless ocean, which carried a golden egg; from this egg Brahma, the first father and creator of the world was born and from the halves of the egg-shell he made the earth and sky, kept apart by the air. Brahma then fixed the floating earth with rocks and mountains and when the earth was ready drew from himself thought, hearing, sight, touch, smell and taste, and blended them to make living things. To each he gave gifts of the senses, the ability to reproduce and the power of movement; the only thing which he did not pass on was thought, this Brahma kept to himself.

Having kept the world at this stage for many ages, Brahma divided himself and created Sarasvati, goddess of knowledge and the arts, with whom he fell in love. To avoid Brahma's loving gaze, Sarasvati would move aside but he would grow a new head in order to see her still. After he had grown four heads facing in each direction, she soared into the air and Brahma grew a fifth head looking upwards. He then begged her to help him create angels, devils and humans for the earth. They married and after one hundred years the first human was born and was given the gifts of the senses, reproduction, movement and intelligent thought. Brahma's fifth head was destroyed by Shiva, goddess of destruction, and he now remains in space, rides swans or peacocks on earth or sits beside Sarasvati. The world now belongs to humans and living creatures, overlooked by the Gods, angels and demons, helping or punishing them as appropriate.

Brahma with his five heads.

English Heritage Education Service/Peter Dunn

Resource Sheet 3 *(continued)*

P'an-Ku, the first being according to Chinese ideas on creation.

English Heritage Education Service/Peter Dunn

CHINA

In the beginning was Chaos in the form of a hen's egg inside of which were the opposing forces of yin and yang. Yin is negative, cold, dark, heavy and feminine, yang is positive, warm, bright, light and masculine. Then one day the egg was split apart by these forces and the heavy elements formed the earth and the lighter ones the sky. Between the two was the first being, P'an-ku, with a pair of horns and tusks and covered with thick hair. He kept the earth and the sky apart for 18,000 years separating them a little further as he grew. His mood controlled the weather; when he was happy it was fine, when he was angry, a storm blew up. There are two versions of what happened later. Some people say that he died exhausted and his head, stomach, right arm and feet became the mountains in the north, south, east and west, his hair became the trees and plants, his tears became the rivers and seas, his breath the wind, his voice the thunder and his fleas mankind. Others say that with the aid of the dragon (the most important of creatures with scales), the tortoise (the most important of creatures with shells), the unicorn (the most important of creatures with hair) and the phoenix (the most important of creatures with feathers) he chiselled the world into shape and ruled during the first epoch filling mankind with wisdom. When he had done this he vanished.

ANCIENT EGYPT

The Egyptians believed that in the beginning were the endless, dark and silent waters of chaos in the depths of which was the formless spirit, the creator Nun. There are many different versions of the creation of the world but according to one, there was in the water a single perfect lotus bud inside of which slept the baby sun – Ra. As the bud opened, Ra awoke sending out rays of sunlight. Immediately he grew into a prince and his children were formed – Air (Shu) and Moisture (Tefenet); they then gave birth to Sky (Nut) above the sea and Earth (Geb) scattered across it. Dazzled by the glare from sunbeams on the water as he looked down on his creation, drops from his eyes fell to earth becoming all the living things – insects, animals, birds, fish and man. Since they were born from tears, tears and sorrow were in their nature, with quarrelling and fighting.

Man was the worst and finally enraged Ra with his arrogance; plucking out one of his eyes he hurled it across the Earth, burning the crops and ground and destroying the human race with plague. With only one eye, however, Ra grew old and wandered in the underworld, unable to give earth light. Darkness ruled until Ra's offspring offered help. Earth and Air lay down and Sky covered them face down stretching so she reached the horizon in the east and in the west. Then, raising her back, she formed an arch-shape and was fixed in place for eternity supported by Air and the Earth became fertile again.

Ra, rejuvenated from the perfume of the lotus flower which bloomed in the darkness, would start each day at the eastern horizon, and over 12 hours would travel along the arch of Sky's body, rewarding the good on earth with light and heat and punishing the wicked with drought. At the end of the day, Ra, old once again, would step onto a silver boat and be carried through the underworld

until he once again breathed the scent of the lotus flower and created another day.

English Heritage Education Service/Peter Dunn

The Egyptian theory of creation.

EDUCATIONAL APPROACHES

Telling the story

The creation stories from different societies can be a useful way of encouraging younger children to think about the whole question of where we come from, and why Darwin's ideas were so surprising to his contemporaries. They also provide a fertile resource for storytelling, drama and creative art work, and can be linked to a variety of history topics.

Choose one of the stories to tell to your pupils. After telling the story for the first time, ask them what they can remember about it, and record their responses on a flip chart. Encourage them to think about sequencing and chronology. Tell the story again and ask them to check the points they recalled as they listen. Then, working in pairs, ask them to choose six or eight main events to create a storyboard, then to retell the story to their partner. The story can then be presented in dramatic or dance/mime form, with the pupils working in small groups, and performing to the rest of the class.

RESPONSES TO DARWIN'S THEORY

The publication of Darwin's ideas generated a very large response, ranging from the letters and articles of fellow scientists, academics and institutions to popular newspaper reports and cartoonists' interpretations. A great deal of this material still survives, and can be used in the classroom as documentary evidence for the impact of Darwin's theories on his contemporaries. A selection of this material, which you may copy to use in the classroom, follows in this chapter. You may prefer to use only short extracts with younger pupils or those with reading difficulties.

Letter to Darwin from the naturalist and clergyman Leonard Jenyns (only part of the letter survives, and this is an extract from the surviving part).

My dear Darwin,   *Jan. 4. 1860*
I have read your interesting book with all carefulness as you enjoined, – have gleaned a great deal from it, & consider it one of the most valuable contributions to Nat. Hist Literature of the present day. Perhaps you may like to know what I think of your particular theory .... You will see that I embrace yr theory in part, but hardly to the full extent to which you carry it. Still I allow you have made out a very strong case, and I will not pretend to say what future researches in the same direction may not ultimately establish. . . . . .
One great difficulty to my mind in the way of your theory is the fact of the existence of Man. I was beginning to think you had entirely passed over this question, till almost in the last page I find you saying that 'light will be thrown on the origin of man & his history'. By this I suppose is meant that he is to be considered a modified & no doubt greatly improved orang! I doubt if this will find acceptance with the generality of readers – I am not one of those in the habit of mixing up questions of science & scripture, but I can hardly see what sense or meaning is to be attached to <u>Gen</u>: 2.7 & yet more to vv. 21.22, of the same chapter, giving an account of the creation of <u>woman</u>, – if the human species at least has not been created independently of other animals, but merely come into the world by ordinary descent from previously existing races – whatever those races may be supposed to have been. Neither can I easily bring myself to the idea that man's reasoning faculties & above all his <u>moral sense,</u> cd ever have been obtained from irrational progenitors, by mere natural selection – acting however gradually & for whatever length of time that may be required. This seems to be doing away altogether with the Divine Image which forms the insurmountable distinction between man and brutes.

Letter to Darwin from T. H. Huxley.   *Jermyn S.*
                                                                                   Nov. 23d 1859

My dear Darwin
I finished your book yesterday a lucky examination having furnished me with a few hours of continuous leisure. . . . Nothing I think can be better than the tone of the book – it impresses those who know nothing about the subject.
As for your doctrines I am prepared to go to the Stake if requisite in support of Chap. IX. & most part of Chaps. X, XI, XII & Chap XIII. contains much that is most admirable, but on one or two points I enter a caveat until, I can see further into all sides of this question.
As to the first four chapters I agree thoroughly & fully with all the principles laid down in them – I think you have demonstrated a true cause for the production of species...
I trust you will not allow yourself to be in any way disgusted or annoyed by the considerable abuse & misrepresentation which unless I greatly mistake is in store for you – Depend upon it you have earned the lasting gratitude of all thoughtful men – and as to the curs which will bark & yelp – you must recollect that some of your friends at any rate are endowed with an amount of combativeness which (though you have often & justly rebuked it) may stand you in good stead.
I am sharpening up my claws & beak in readiness ...

Ever yours faithfully
T H Huxley

The Times, Monday, December 26th, 1859

Darwin on the Origin of Species by T. H. Huxley (extract).

'...We must weigh this hypothesis strictly in the controversy which is coming, by the only tests which are appropriate, and by no others whatsoever.

The hypothesis to which we point, and of which the present work of Mr Darwin is but the preliminary outline, may be stated in his own language as follows: '*Species originated by means of natural selection, or through the preservation of the favoured races in the struggle for life...*'

Its author, Mr Darwin, inheritor of a once celebrated name, won his spurs in science when most of those now distinguished were young men, and has for the last 20 years held a place in the front ranks of British philosophers. After a circumnavigatory voyage undertaken solely for the love of his science, Mr Darwin published a series of researches which at once arrested the attention of naturalists and geologists ...More recently Mr Darwin, with a versatility which is among the rarest of gifts, turned his attention to a most difficult question of zoology and minute anatomy; and no living naturalist and anatomist has published a better monograph than that which resulted from his labours. Such a man, at all events, has not entered the sanctuary with unwashed hands, and when he lays before us the results of 20 years' investigation and reflection we must listen even though we be disposed to strike. But, in reading his work it must be confessed that the attention which might at first be dutifully, soon becomes willingly, given, so clear is the author's thought, so outspoken his conviction, so honest and fair the candid expression of his doubts. Those who would judge the book must read it...

But there is, at all events, one advantage possessed by the more recent writer over his predecessor [Lamarck]. Mr Darwin abhors mere speculation as nature abhors a vacuum. He is as greedy of cases and precedents as any constitutional lawyer, and all the principles he lays down are capable of being brought to the test of observation and experiment...'

Letter to Darwin from the botanist H. C. Watson (extracts).

Thames Ditton
21 Nov [1859]

My dear Sir,
Once commenced to read the 'Origin' I could not rest till I had galloped through the whole. I shall now begin to re-read it more deliberately. meantime I am tempted to write you the first impressions, not doubting that they will in the main be the permanent impressions.
...your leading idea will assuredly become recognized as an established truth in science, i.e. 'natural selection'. – (it has the characteristics of all great natural truths, clarifying what was obscure, simplifying what was intricate, adding greatly to previous knowledge. You are the greatest Revolutionist in natural history of this century, if not of all centuries.
... Now these novel views are brought before the scientific public, it seems truly remarkable how so many of them could have failed to see their right road sooner
...A quarter century ago you & I must have been in something like the same state of mind, on the main question. But you were able to see & work out the quo modo of the succession, the all important thing, while I failed to grasp it ...a quarter of a century ago, I was also one of the few who then doubted the absolute distinctness of species & special creations of them. Yet I, like the rest, failed to detect the quo modo which was reserved for your penetration to discover, & by your discernment to apply.
...But how greatly this, with your chronology of animal life, will shock the ideas of many men!

very sincerely
Hewett C. Watson

Review of *On the Origin of Species* in *The Quarterly Review* vol 108, July – October 1860, by Samuel Wilberforce

'Any contribution to our Natural History literature from the pen of Mr C. Darwin is certain to command attention. His scientific attainments, his insight and carefulness as an observer, blended with no scanty measure of imaginative sagacity, and his clear and lively style, make all his writings unusually attractive. His present volume on the 'Origin of Species' is the result of many years observation, thought, and speculation; and is manifestly regarded by him as the 'opus' upon which his future fame is to rest...

The essay is full of Mr Darwin's characteristic excellences. It is a most readable book; full of facts in natural history, old and new, of his collecting and of his observing... It assumes, too, the grave proportions of a sustained argument upon a matter of the deepest interest, not to naturalists only, or even to men of science exclusively, but to everyone who is interested in the history of man and of the relations of nature around him to the history and plan of creation.

With Mr Darwin's 'argument' we may say in the outset that we shall have much and grave fault to find.

...Mr Darwin writes as a Christian, and we doubt not that he is one. We do not for one moment believe him to be one of those who retain in some corner of their hearts a secret unbelief which they dare not vent; and we therefore pray him to consider well the grounds on which we brand his speculations with the charge of such a tendency. First, then, he not obscurely declares that he applies his scheme of the action of the principle of natural selection to MAN himself, as well as to the animals around him. Now, we must say at once, and openly, that such a notion is absolutely incompatible not only with single expressions in the word of God on that subject of natural science with which it is not immediately concerned, but, which in our judgement is of far more importance, with the whole representation of that moral and spiritual condition of man which is its proper subject-matter. Man's derived supremacy over the earth; man's power of articulate speech; man's gift of reason; man's free-will and responsibility; man's fall and man's redemption; the incarnation of the Eternal Son; the indwelling of the Eternal Spirit, – all are equally and utterly irreconcilable with the degrading notion of the brute origin of him who was created in the image of God, and redeemed by the Eternal Son assuming to himself his nature.'

A contemporary view of Darwin.

A satirical view of Darwin's theories.

The wife of the Bishop of Worcester expressed Wilberforce's final point rather more succinctly when when she said: 'Descended from the apes? My dear, let us hope that it is not true, but if it is, let us pray that it will not become generally known.'

EDUCATIONAL APPROACHES

Using documentary sources

Ask your pupils to look at each written extract in turn, and to decide whether the writer was in full support of Darwin's ideas, generally sympathetic, undecided, or in disagreement. What evidence does each author use to support his point of view? Ask pupils to consider the language used in each extract. Is the writer trying to persuade the reader to his point of view or is he merely stating his case? If he is trying to persuade, how successful do your pupils think the writer is?

Cartoonists seized on the idea that Darwin supposed man to be descended from the apes with delight – it gave scope for amusing, if predictable, cartoons. In fact, Darwin never claimed that man was directly descended from the apes, rather that man and the apes had a common ancestor.

A parody in *Punch,* based on the famous anti-slavery medallion which asked 'Am I not a man and a brother?' (see below).

Evolution of a goose into a donkey. Cartoons such as these show how Darwin's ideas were misunderstood by a great many people.

Wedgwood medallion from an illustration in Erasmus Darwin's *The Botanic Garden.*

Charles Darwin – notice his hand and foot.

MAN·IS·BVT·A·WORM.

'Man is but a worm'. This *Punch* cartoon shows the evolutionary processes as a simple series of steps from chaos and the worm, through various 'ape stages' to the end result of Victorian man complete with top hat.

DARWIN AND INHERITANCE

One of Darwin's greatest problems was that of inheritance. A criticism of natural selection was the belief that characteristics of parents would be blended in the offspring; Darwin had no answer to this. Had he known of the work, in the 1860s, of the Czech monk and physicist Gregor Mendel (1822- 1884), he would have known that this was not the case.

With the aim of improving crop production, Mendel conducted experiments on plants, but instead of examining the plants as a whole, he studied single characteristics which differed from one another in an either/or manner; garden peas for example were either tall or short and their seeds were either yellow or green – there were no intermediate types. Using peas (which normally self-fertilise) Mendel cross-pollinated the different varieties producing a hybrid generation which were then self-fertilised. He found that:

■ when a tall plant was crossed with a dwarf plant the offspring were all tall

■ when these offspring were then crossed the offspring were tall or dwarf in a ratio of 3:1.

Similarly he found that when a yellow-seeded pea was crossed with a green-seeded pea the first generation was all yellow, but the second generation was yellow or green in a ratio of 3:1. There were no in-between colours. In other words there was no blending of the characteristics. The diagram explains this type of inheritance using the example of wild mice which may be either brown 'mouse' coloured or black.

In humans most inheritance is much more complicated than this but there are some characteristics which occur in an either/or manner;

Earlobes may be free (dominant) or attached (recessive), and there may be the ability or inability to curl the tongue (dominant) and the inability (recessive).

Instead, Darwin developed the theory of 'Pangenesis'. In this he proposed that each organ of the body gave a representative set of microscopic particles or 'gemmules' which were collected in the reproductive organs. The offspring, therefore, tended to resemble both its parents, sometimes more, sometimes less, according to how the gemmules were reassorted. Darwin mostly used this to explain the origin of variations, or why every individual is different, and also to explain some of the odd things about inheritance such as certain characteristics jumping generations or running in the family. Pangenesis also helped him explain those cases where it looked as if acquired characteristics could be inherited. Like Lamarck, Darwin wrongly believed that some characteristics or habits gained during a lifetime could be passed on to the next generation.

The German naturalist August Weismann, however, believed the theory of the inheritance of acquired characteristics to be wrong and could find no evidence of it ever having occurred. He had amputated mouse tails for 20 generations with no effect. From the late 1870s, with the increasing microscopic knowledge of cell structure and function, he showed that the hereditary substance or 'germ plasm' was passed on from generation to generation, regardless of acquired bodily changes. By1885 he had recognised the nucleus

of the sex cells to be the carrier of the hereditary material, with both the male and female making equal contributions to the fertilised egg. The physical characteristics of an organism (phenotype) are dependent on two factors: the inherited genetic information (the genotype) and the conditions affecting it throughout its life.

Weismann's work at the end of the nineteenth century had laid the foundations for the rediscovery of Mendel's work in 1900. Initially this led to a further decline in Darwin's reputation as the either/or characterises seemed to oppose the Darwin's idea of continuous minute variations on which natural selection could work. Mendelian geneticists (the term gene was coined for the hereditary particles in 1909) believed that evolution was now characterised by abrupt transformations or 'mutation'. This meant that sudden changes in the genotype resulted in equally large changes in the phenotype, and natural selection was therefore of negligible influence. The two views remained opposed to each other for thirty years, until work by geneticists showed that large mutations were the exception rather than the rule and sexual reproduction provided an almost endless source of minute variations which could add up to a large effect.

By 1911 the work of Thomas Hunt Morgan on fruit flies had show that the genes were located on the chromosomes situated in the nucleus at the centre of every cell and that most characteristics were controlled by many genes. During the 1940s and 1950s chromosomes were discovered to contain Deoxyribonucleic acid (DNA) and protein, and it was in 1953, when James Watson and Francis Crick worked out the structure of the DNA molecule, that heredity was really understood.

EDUCATIONAL APPROACHES

Ask pupils to bring in photographs of family members – parents, grandparents, and siblings and in pairs ask them to suggest what characteristics have been inherited. (It is often easier to see resemblances in someone else's family, rather than your own which you are too familiar with). Certain characteristics may have skipped a generation and pupils may be more similar to grandparents than parents.

Demonstrate the Mendelian genetics with the ability to roll the tongue which is inherited on an either/or basis; the ability to roll the tongue is dominant, the inability is recessive. Or with ear lobes; a detached ear lobe is a dominant feature; joined is recessive.

Ask pupils to check with their parents, grandparents and even, if possible, great-grandparents whether they have the ability to roll the tongue, (or alternatively, detached or attached earlobes).

Ask them to chart their findings, in family tree format. Can they see any pattern? Has the tendency appeared in each generation or has it skipped one? Are all those in the same generation able to demonstrate the same tendency?

Dominant and recessive genes

Each mouse has two genes for fur colour, one inherited from each parent. The genes may either be brown 'mouse' colour (B) or black (b) The gene combination of an individual therefore may be one of three types:

Two brown genes (**BB**) – a mouse with these genes will be brown

Two black genes (**bb**) – a mouse with these genes will be black

One of each (**Bb**) – a mouse with these genes will be brown because the **B** gene is dominant, hiding the **b** gene which is recessive

First generation

If two brown mice both with **BB** genes are crossed, each mouse pass on an **B** gene to the offspring and they will all be brown (**BB**).

If two black mice with **bb** genes are crossed the offspring will all be black (**bb**).

If a brown mouse (**BB**) is crossed with a black mouse (**bb**) the offspring will receive a gene from each and will have the genes **Bb** and hence have brown fur since the brown gene is dominant.

Second generation

If two of the Bb mice are then crossed there are four possible combinations of the genes

BB
Brown

Bb
Brown

bB
Brown

bb
Black

Thus in the second generation by crossing two brown mice with **Bb** genes, on average three out of every four offspring will be brown; one will be black. This is the Mendelian ratio of 3:1.

THE DEBATE CONTINUES

The name Charles Darwin and the theory of natural selection today regularly appear in the daily newspapers both in connection with evolutionary issues, seemingly unrelated topics and advertisements. As can be seen from the following articles the controversy between religion and evolution still exists today.

Ask your pupils to collect newspaper cuttings of articles about Darwin or references to his ideas. They could keep a cuttings file.

Vatican's slow evolution as it discovers Darwin

Andrew Brown

One hundred and thirty eight years after the publication of Darwin's *Origin of Species*, and 6,000 years since the creation of the world as calculated by Archbishop Ussher, the Roman Catholic Church has acknowledged the theory of evolution as true.

The Vatican yesterday published a letter from Pope John Paul II to a group of scientific experts in which he said: "new knowledge leads us to recognise in the theory of evolution more than a hypothesis ... The convergence, of results of work done independently one from the other, constitutes a significant argument in favour of this theory."

However, the Pope's letter continues to resist the doctrine that the human spirit arose as the result of unaided natural processes, or that human consciousness is not a distinct and important factor in the world. There are "spiritual readings of evolution", he wrote, as well as "materialistic and reductionist

In the beginning: Charles Darwin, and the Pope

ones", and the faithful must distinguish between them.

"[Even] if the origin of the human body is sought in living matter which existed before it, the spiritual soul is directly created by God ... Consequently, the theories of evolution, which consider the spirit as emerging from forces of living matter or as a simple epiphenomenon of this matter, are incompatible with the truth about man."

The Pope's acknowledgement of the truth of the evolutionary, scientific view of the world's history ends a long rearguard action fought by the Roman Catholic Church to maintain some literal sense for the book of Genesis. In 1950, Pope Pius XII allowed Catholics to believe in the truth of evolution, although he insisted that it was not proven, and that full weight should be given to the arguments against it.

He also maintained that the

Genesis account of creation, though "not conforming to the historical method used by the best Greek and Latin writers or by competent authors of our time" nevertheless "pertained to history in a true sense".

In particular, Pius XII claimed that Catholics must believe there was a literal Adam, a first man from whom all subsequent humans descend, and all of whose ancestors were beasts. This, he thought, was necessary in order to preserve the doctrine of original sin.

It is not clear whether this teaching still binds Catholics: the catechism says only that the account of the fall in Genesis 3 uses figurative language, but affirms a primeval event, a deed that took place at the beginning of the history of man."

The Independent
25 October 1996

"The Pope's acknowledgement of the truth of the evolutionary, scientific view of the world's history ends a long rearguard action fought by the Roman Catholic Church to maintain some literal sense for the book of Genesis."

Americans are throwing the book at Darwin again. And it's not just the Bible. Or the law. The new creationists are waging a war to have their own theory as accepted as the scientific orthodoxy of evolution. **Ian Katz** reports

Monkey retrial

God and Darwin . . . the view from Britain

RICHARD HARRIES
Bishop of Oxford

DARWINIAN theory is not only compatable with belief in God but I find it enriches and deepens my understanding of how the Lord creates. Evolution shows God creates by process, as opposed to "ready made". The evolutionary theory has largely been accepted by the Church since the 1880s. My predecessor Samuel Wilberforce, clerical protagonist in the debate with Huxley, Darwin's champion, was a keen amateur scientist and felt the evidence for the theory at the time was insubstantial — he didn't reject it out of hand.

Scrabbling around for evidence disproving evolutionary theory strikes me as a waste of time — religious people should be doing better things.

PETER MAY
Lay member, General Synod

I THINK the creationists are profoundly mistaken. To try to read natural evidence in the way they suggest leaves you with one of two conclusions. Either the fossil evidence is a deliberate deception by God, which raises questions about His character and motives, or you have to dismiss the efficacy of carbon-dating techniques to suggest that dinosaurs where roaming the Earth only 10,000 years time. It's a total scientific muddle. This counter argument undermines the whole question of whether life has meaning and value. This is the central question we should all be asking, not hurling the Christian world view on to the scrapheap.

RICHARD DAWKINS
Author of The Selfish Gene

"PROGRESSIVE" creationists will be as much of an embarrassment to educated religious people as the superficially more naive "Young Earthers". Anybody who is persuaded by the analogy of 'John loves Mary' written in the sand has not begun to understand Darwinism. The starting point of the Darwinian view is that *no* theory that relies upon chance can explain living creatures. Why is it so hard for people to grasp the elementary fact that Darwinism is *not* a theory of chance? It is about as far from chance as you can get.

> **"Polls consistently show that around half of Americans consider Genesis a more plausible account of their beginning than The Origin of Species."**

INHERIT The Wind, the 1955 dramatisation of the infamous Scopes Monkey Trial, is playing again on Broadway. The play has long been a staple of small town theatres and one more revival, albeit one starring George C Scott, might have gone all but unnoticed. However, the new production has been vested with an unusual edge. For 71 years after John Scopes was fined $100 for teaching evolution in his Tennessee classroom, the battle over man's origins is raging once more across America.

The Tennessee legislature spent [a month arguing over a proposed]

embrace Darwinism's lexicon of natural selection and random mutation than their European cousins. Polls consistently show that around half of Americans consider Genesis a more plausible account of their beginnings than The Origin Of Species. What is new is the aggressive effort by creationists to have their own "theory" accorded similar institutional respect to the scientific orthodoxy of evolution. "The important part is that we're getting it on the table." says Mark Hartwig of the Foundation for Thought and Ethics, a Texas-based Christian group which produces creationist literature.

To some extent the resurgence of [...] tian Coalition. the evangelicals have set about returning Genesis to what they consider its rightful place in the classroom. Even secular Republican politicians have been weary of alienating religious voters by rallying to Darwin's side.

But there is more to the current counter evolutionary mood than politics. Darwin's detractors have been able to surf a wave of anti scientific sentiment in America highlighted by last week's capture of the suspected Unabomber. While only an unhinged few would defend the murderous tactics allegedly used by the reclusive former mathematician many Americans admitted to [...]

stories of UFO ab[...] dismissed as poppy[...] with fancy deg[...] jackets The talk [...] seller lists are fille[...] about the existen[...] ghosts.

The creationists[...] smartened up th[...] their message t[...] ies. creationism [...] the so-called Ne[...] ably evangelica[...] claimed that th[...] panoply of life [...] in six 24 hour d[...] Genesis They [...] Earth's assemb[...]

The Guardian 11 April 1996
Monkey retrial

Ian Katz

'Creationism is showing its muscle again, as it did more than 70 years ago in the in southern town of Dayton, scene of the famous Monkey Trial [where John Scopes was fined $100 for teaching evolution in his Tennessee classroom]

…The Tennessee legislature spent last month arguing over a proposed law to ban the teaching of evolution as fact. In the end, the bill, which would have allowed for the dismissal of any teacher who refused to characterise evolution as a theory, was narrowly voted down.

The little southern state is by no means an isolated hotbed of creationism. In neighbouring Alabama, high school biology textbooks will soon carry a disclaimer that evolution is 'a controversial theory', while every

science teacher in the state will be issued a copy of Darwin on Trial, a popular creationist text by Berkeley law professor Phillip Johnson. In one Georgia county, teachers were ordered recently to offer students a variety of theories on the origins of life. In New Hampshire, a bill under consideration would make it illegal to teach evolution without parental consent.

… New Worlders or not, Americans have always been less willing to embrace Darwinism's lexicon of natural selection and random mutation than their European cousins. Polls consistently show that around half of Americans consider Genesis a more plausible account of their beginning than The Origin of Species. What is new is the aggressive effort by creationists to have their own 'theory' accorded similar institutional respect to the scientific orthodoxy of evolution.

…Recently a new generation of creationists have espoused a more

subtle, less easily ridiculed, variation on the old Genesis theme. …The argument is simple: even the most basic building blocks of life are so complex that they could not have come about without the influence of some guiding intelligence.

Of Pandas and People, a popular glossy textbook produced by the Foundation for Thought and Ethics, puts it like this: 'When we find 'John Loves Mary' written in the sand we assume it resulted from an intelligent cause …To say that DNA and protein arose by natural causes, as chemical evolution does, is to say complex, coded messages arose by natural causes. It is akin to saying 'John loves Mary' arose from the action of the waves, or from the interaction of the grains of sand. It is like saying the painting of a sunset arose spontaneously from the atoms in the paint and canvas.'……

The Guardian 16 January 1997

A tall story
Stuart Blackman

Everyone knows why the giraffe has a long neck. Well it's obvious, isn't it? As every biology textbook will tell you, a long neck allows a giraffe to browse on foliage that is out of reach of the competition.

It is perhaps because it is so obvious, and something that all parties can agree on, that everyone from Darwin and Lamarck to religious fundamentalists have used the giraffe's neck to illustrate their own theories for the diversity of life, leading it to become a common currency in evolutionary debate.

But, in the latest issue of the journal American Naturalist, zoologists Robert Simmons and Lue Scheepers have stuck their own necks out by suggesting that the obvious explanation is in fact quite wrong. For a start, despite giraffes' ability to reach the highest branches, they are only rarely observed feeding at full stretch. Most of the time they browse with their necks held horizontally.

Also, if height is what the giraffes are after, increasing neck length is a very inefficient way of going about it because of the extra work the heart has to do to pump blood up to the brain. But, compared to their shorter ancestors, modern giraffes have increased neck length more than leg length, implying that there is a specific advantage to having a long neck rather than overall height.

Simmons and Scheepers think the answer lies in the unique way that males fight for dominance, behaviour known as 'necking'. Two rivals stand side by side and exchange blows by swinging their well-armoured heads at each other, like clubs. Since the energy delivered by a club increases with both the mass of the head and the length of the shaft, males with longer necks have a better chance of laying out their their opponents.

To support the new theory, the zoologists show that the males with the biggest necks are dominant and get chosen more frequently by receptive females. For animals of the same body mass, males' necks are heavier than females', and their heads are more heavily armoured.

There is also evidence, as is found in many traits that help the bearer compete for dominance or attract mates, that the massive necks and heads of males are actually a hindrance in everyday life, since males are more likely than females to be taken by lions. But, if a long neck is an advantage in fights, and if female giraffes don't fight, why do the females also have long necks? Simmons and Scheepers argue that female giraffes have long necks for the same reason that men have nipples. Males and females develop along very similar pathways, so characteristics that are advantageous in one sex will often be expressed in the other. All of which leaves just one question: why DO birds have wings?

---

briefing

EVOLUTION
Study of lizards proves Darwin was right

Scientists believe they have proved Charles Darwin was right by setting lizards on different evolutionary paths and watching the results. Darwin argued in The Origin of the Species that when organisms colonise a new territory they adapt to its conditions and eventually evolve into a new species.

The first observable evidence that this happens has come from an experiment in which Anolis lizards were introduced to a group of Bahamian islands. Returning to the islands 14 years later, the scientists, led by Dr Jonathan Losos from Washington University, Missouri, found that the island lizards had changed to suit the vegetation of their new environment.

They had developed much shorter hind limbs and become lighter to help them perch on the thinner branches and twigs found on the islands. They also had wider toe-pads than lizards living in their natural home on the island of Staniel Cay.

Science journal Nature, which published the results today, said: "This may be among the most important work in evolutionary studies since Darwin studied the diversity of finches on the Galapagos Islands during the voyage of the Beagle."

The Independent,
2 May 1997

> "To support the new theory, the zoologists show that the males with the biggest necks are dominant and get chosen more frequently by receptive females."

Darwin theory wins by a short leg

BY NIGEL HAWKES
SCIENCE EDITOR

THE evolution of lizards on a group of tiny Caribbean islands has given Darwin's evolutionary theories a leg-up.

Fourteen years after lizards were introduced to the islands, they were found to have adapted to local conditions in the ways that natural selection would have predicted. Hind legs had become shorter so that they could perch successfully on the islands' thinner plant stems and branches. The more the vegetation differed from the island where the lizards originated, the shorter their legs became.

The study shows how quickly a species can adapt to circumstances. Critics of Darwinism often claim that few such examples have been documented.

In 1977 and 1981, members of the lizard species Anolis sagrei, were taken from the island of Stanley Cay — which has reasonably large trees — and transferred in groups of five or ten to 14 other uninhabited islands where there were no other lizards. Earlier studies by Jonathan Losos, of Washington University in St Louis, had shown that the size of lizards' hind limbs depended on the size of the branches they perched on. Those perching on narrow branches or twigs tended to be small, with short hind limbs, but on bigger trees the creatures had longer limbs, making them swifter to escape predators.

The assumption was that the move would lead to an evolutionary trend to smaller limbs, and that is exactly what Dr Losos reports in this week's Nature. On the smallest islands, no lizards survived, but on the larger ones they flourished. One island had more than 700. This rate of evolution is hundreds or thousands of times faster than seen in the fossil record, but comparably rapid evolution has been seen in studies of fish moved from their habitat.

Extract from
The Times,
10 May 1997

BIBLIOGRAPHY

Books are listed under topic headings. Those suitable for use by pupils are marked ★

CHARLES DARWIN'S PUBLICATIONS

Journal and Remarks, Henry Colburn, 1839. reprinted as *Journal of Researches into the Geology and Natural History of the Various Countries visited by H.M.S. 'Beagle'*, 1845.

The Structure and Distribution of Coral Reefs, Smith, Elder, 1842.

Geological Observations on the Volcanic Islands visited during the Voyage of H. M. S. 'Beagle', Smith, Elder, 1844.

Geological Observations on South America, Smith, Elder, 1846.

A Monograph on the Sub-Class Cirripedia 2 vols, Ray Society (1851-1854).

A Monograph on the Fossil Lepadidae, or, Pedunculated Cirripedies of Great Britain, Palaeontographical Society, 1851.

A Monograph on the Fossil Balanidae and Verrucidae of Great Britain, Palaeontographical Society, 1854.

On the Origin of Species by means of Natural Selection, or the Preservation of Favoured Races in the Struggle for Life, Murray, 1859.

On the Various Contrivances by which British and Foreign Orchids are Fertilised by Insects, Murray, 1862.

The Variation of Animals and Plants under Domestication, 1868.

The Descent of Man, and Selection in relation to Sex, 2 vols, Murray, 1871.

The Expression of the Emotions in Man and Animals, Murray, 1872.

The Movements and Habits of Climbing Plants, Murray, 2nd ed 1875 (first edition appeared in the ninth volume of the 'Journal of the Linnean Society').

Insectivorous Plants, 1875.

The Effects of Cross and Self Fertilisation in the Vegetable Kingdom, Murray, 1876.

The Different Forms of Flowers on Plants of the Same Species, Murray, 1877.

The Power of Movement in Plants, Murray, 1880.

The Formation of Vegetable Mould, through the Action of Worms, with Observations on their Habits. Murray, 1881.

SHORT BIOGRAPHIES OF CHARLES DARWIN

Charles Darwin, *The Autobiography of Charles Darwin*, Ed N. Barlow, Collins, 1958.

F. D. Fletcher, *Darwin*, Shire Publications, 1975, ISBN 0-85263-523-0.

R. C. Olby, *Charles Darwin*, Oxford University Press, 1967.

A. Sproule, *Charles Darwin*, Exley Publications, 1990, ISBN 1-85015-213-6.

C. Twist, *Charles Darwin on the Trail of Evolution*, Evans Brothers Ltd, 1993, ISBN 0-237-51264-5.

DETAILED BIOGRAPHIES

P. J. Bowler, *Charles Darwin. The Man and his Influence*, Cambridge University Press, 1990, ISBN 0-521-56668-1.

J. Browne, *Charles Darwin: Voyaging*, (vol 1 of a biography) Jonathan Cape, 1995, ISBN 0-224-04202-5.

A. Desmond and J. Moore, *Darwin* (London: Michael Joseph, 1991) reprinted Penguin, 1992, ISBN 0-14-013192-2.

R. Milner, *Charles Darwin: Evolution of a Naturalist*, Facts on File, 1994, ISBN 0-8160-2557-6.

DOWN HOUSE

Sir Hedley Atkins, *Down: The Home of the Darwins*, Royal College of Surgeons, 1974.

G. Raverat, *Period Piece*, Faber, 1952, ISBN 0-571-06742-5.

DARWIN'S ILLNESS

R. Colp, *To be an Invalid*, University of Chicago Press, 1977, ISBN 0-226-11401-5.

THE BEAGLE VOYAGE

C. Darwin, *Voyage of the Beagle*, Edited by J. Browne and M. Neve, Penguin, 1989, ISBN 0-14-043268-X.

C. Darwin, *Beagle Diary*, edited by R. Keynes, Cambridge University Press, 1988, ISBN 0-521-23503-0.

A. Moorehead, *Darwin and the Beagle*, Hamish Hamilton, 1969, ISBN 24-0173-9.

K. S. Thomson, *H.M.S. Beagle: The Story of Mr Darwin's Ship*, W. W. Norton, 1995, ISBN 0-393-03778-9.

DARWIN'S THEORIES AND EVOLUTION

B. Cork and L Bresler, *Young Scientist Book of Evolution*, Usborn, 1985 ISBN 0-86020-867-2.★

C. Darwin, *On the origin of species*, edited by J. W. Burrow, Penguin, 1968, ISBN 0-14-043205-1, ISBN 0-14-043205-1.

R. Dawkins, *The Blind Watchmaker*, Penguin, 1988, ISBN 0-14-14481-1.

C. Darwin, *The Illustrated Origin of Species*, Abridged and Introduced by R. E. Leakey, Faber and Faber, 1979, ISBN 0-571-11477-6.

Linda Gamlin, *Eyewitness Science. Evolution*, Dorling Kindersley, 1993, ISBN 0-7513-1015-8.★

Jonathan Miller and Borin van Loon, *Darwin for Beginners*. Icon Books, 1992, ISBN 1-874166-01-3.

Richard Milner, *The Encyclopedia of Evolution*, Henry Holt and Company, 1990, ISBN 0-805027-17-3

J. Solomon, *Evolution and the Human Population*, Blackwell, 1983, ISBN 0-631-91990-2.

BACKGROUND READING

Medicine in the nineteenth century

I. Dawson and I. Coulson, *Medicine and Health through Time*, John Murray, 1996, ISBN: 0-7195-5265-6.★

A. M. Gray with N. Smith, *Medical Care and Health*, Oxford University Press, 1996, ISBN 0-19-917247-1.

The Victorians

D. Evans, *How We Used to Live: Victorians, Early and Late*, A & C Black in association with Yorkshire Television, ISBN 0-7136-3310-7.★

M. Sharman, *The Victorian Years*, Evans Brothers, 1993, ISBN 0-237-51291- 2.

R. Wood, *Family Life in Victorian Britain*, Wayland, 1994, ISBN 0-7502-1008- 7.★

Ships

C. Booth, *Ships*, Heinemann Educational Books, 1983, ISBN 0-435-31070-4.★

R. Coote, *The Sailor through History*, Wayland, 1993, ISBN 0-7502-0435-4.★

A. Hamilton-MacLaren, *Water Transport*, Wayland, 1991, ISBN 0-7502-0161-4.★

D. Roberts, *The Superbook of Ships*, Kingfisher, 1985, ISBN 0-86272-175-X.★

The Visual Dictionary of Ships and Sailing, Dorling Kindersley, 1991, ISBN 0- 86318-702-1.★

Making maps

P. Chrisp, *Mapping the Unknown*, Wayland, 1996, ISBN 0-7502-1384-1.★

D. Lambert, *Maps and Globes*, Wayland, 1986, ISBN 0-85078-624-X.★

Expeditions

R. Matthews, *Explorer* (Eyewitness guides), Dorling Kindersley, 1991, ISBN 0-86318-646-7.★

R. Stefoff, *Scientific Explorers: Travels in Search of Knowledge*, Oxford University Press, 1992, ISBN 0-19-507689-3.

R. Stefoff, *Accidental Explorers: Surprises and Side Trips in the History of Discovery*, Oxford University Press, 1992, ISBN 0-19-507685-0.

Plants

M. Unwin, *Science with Plants*, Usborne, 1992, ISBN 0-7460-0977-1.★

E. Catherall, *Exploring Plants*, Wayland, 1992, 1-85210-911-4.★

Creation stories

H. Cherry and K. McLeish, *In the Beginning: Creation Myths from Around the World*, Longman, 1984, ISBN 0-582-25083-8.★

V. Hamilton, *In the Beginning: Creation Stories from Around the World*, Pavillion Books Ltd, 1992, ISBN 1-85145-865-4.★

M. Mayo, *The Orchard Book of Creation Stories*, Orchard Books, 1995, ISBN 1-85213-774-6.★

N. Philip, *The Illustrated Book of Myths, Tales and Legends of the World*, Dorling Kindersley, 1995, ISBN 0-7513-5317-5.★

Genetics and inheritance

J. Bunting, *Genetics*, Boxtree Ltd, 1994, ISBN 1-85283-337-8.

N Hawkes, *Genetic Engineering*, Aladdin, 1991, ISBN 0-7496-0411-5.

N. Sully, *Looking at Genetics*, Batsford Academic and Educational, 1985, ISBN 0-7134-4775-3.

USING THE HISTORIC ENVIRONMENT

The English Heritage Education on Site series aims to help teachers make best use of the historic environment in all curriculum subjects. The titles listed below all contain ideas and teaching strategies relevant to a study of Charles Darwin, his ideas, journey and life at Down House in the nineteenth century.

S. Allen and S. Wilkinson, *Houses and Homes*, English Heritage, 1997. ISBN 1-85074-398-3.

T. Copeland, *Maths and the Historic Environment*, English Heritage, 1991, ISBN 1-85074-329-0.

I. Davies and C. Webb, *Using Documents*, English Heritage, 1996, ISBN 1- 85074-492-0.

G. Durbin, *Using Historic Houses*, English Heritage, 1993, ISBN, 1-85074- 390-8.

J. Fairclough, *History through Role Play*, English Heritage, 1994, ISBN 1- 85074-478-5.

E. Maddern, *Storytelling at Historic Sites*, English Heritage, 1992, ISBN 1-85074-378-9.

S. Marcus and R. Barker, *Historic Parks and Gardens*, English Heritage, 1997, ISBN 1-85074-510-2.

J. Pownall and N. Hutson, *Science and the Historic Environment*, English Heritage, 1992, ISBN 1-85074-331-2.

PLACES TO VISIT

Down House, Downe, near Orpington, Kent. The home of Charles Darwin for over forty years. Managed by English Heritage.

Linley Sambourne House, 18 Stafford Terrace, Kensington, London. The home of Edward and Marion Sambourne, the house gives and insight into a typical Victorian house. Managed by The Victorian Society.

The Natural History Museum, South Kensington, London, has a gallery called *Origin of Species* in which the theory of evolution is explored in detail.

ACKNOWLEDGMENTS

The author and editor would like to thank Janet Browne, The Wellcome Trust and Donald W. Insall & Associates for their help and support.

Opposite: The Voyage of the Beagle. Photocopy this map for your pupils to play 'Into the Unknown'.

Our Education Service aims to help teachers at all levels make best use of the resource of the historic environment. Educational groups can make free visits to over 400 historic properties in the care of English Heritage. The following booklets are free on request. **Visiting Historic Sites and Buildings** contains a full list of all our sites, details of how to book a visit, and activities for National Curriculum work on site. Our magazine, **Heritage Learning,** is published three times a year. **Resources,** our catalogue, lists all our educational books, videos, posters and slide packs. Please contact:

**English Heritage
Education Service
429 Oxford Street
London W1R 2HD
Tel: 0171 973 3442
Fax: 0171 973 3443
http://www.
english-heritage.org.uk**